# THE SPUNKY PARTS

## of issues 32 to 37

Written, drawn & produced by

**Chris Donald (Editor)**
**Graham Dury Simon Thorp**
**Simon Donald**

With contributions from
**David Jones Graham Murdoch Ray Fury**
**Dave Purnell Martin Langston**

Photography by Colin Davison

Production Assistant Ann Hedley
Executive Head of Administration Maddie McGowan
Executive Head of Administration's Assistant Susan Patterson

**ISBN 1 870 870 15 8**

Published in Great Britain by John Brown Publishing Limited,
The Boathouse, Crabtree Lane, Fulham, London SW6 8NJ

First printing, September 1990, or thereabouts



Printed and bound in Great Britain

# ROGER MELLIE THE MAN ON THE TELLY

ROGER HAS BEEN CALLED INTO THE PRODUCER'S OFFICE

OKAY EVERYBODY...
STANDBY
TAKE TWO!

OKAY! THREE-TWO-ONE, LET'S SPIN THE WHEEL OF FORTUNE! WOULD THE FIRST CONTESTANT LIKE TO STEP UP TO THE OCHE PLEASE!

YOU SEEM TO BE A BIT CONFUSED ROGER. THERE'S NO DARTS, NO SPINNING WHEELS, AND NO "3-2-1". COUNTROUND IS AN **INTELLECTUAL** SHOW
MMM
YOU SEE... IT'S A BIT LIKE SCRABBLE. EACH CONTESTANT HAS TO MAKE A WORD OUT OF THEIR NINE LETTERS. AND THE BIGGEST WORD WINS, OKAY?

PRESENTLY...
BEFORE WE START ROUND ONE, LET'S MEET THE LOVELY CATHY!
APPLAUSE

COME ON THEN LOVE, GIVE US SOME FUCKIN' LETTERS. WE HAVEN'T GOT ALL DAY.
V C

JUST KEEP GOING! WE'LL EDIT THAT OUT LATER!
FTV

OOH... WHAT A LOVELY MOVER!! WHERE DID WE FIND HER, TOM?
V C

SOON...
AND YOUR LAST LETTER IS... **M**
OOOH! WHAT BASTARD LUCK! YOU ONLY NEEDED A 'K' FOR WANK!
W A N M
TIM
MARIO

RIGHT THEN. YOU'VE GOT 30 SECONDS TO MAKE A WORD OUT OF THAT LOT. I'M JUST NIPPING FOR A PISS
S H O T C W A N M
V C
TIM
BACK IN A TICK

TWO MINUTES LATER...
T C W A M N
TIM
MARION

FIVE MINUTES LATER...
SORRY 'BOUT THAT FOLKS. GOT A FEW HAIRS CAUGHT IN ME ZIP
A N M
TIM
YOU KNOW WHAT IT'S LIKE!

RIGHT. LET'S HAVE A LOOK AT THESE WORDS THEN... ERM... YOU WITH THE BEARD... WHAT DID YOU GET?
ROGER
TIM
MARION

MY WORD IS 'STOMACH', ROGER. S-T-O-M-A-C-H
TIM

**THAT'S** NOT HOW YOU SPELL STOMACH!
YES IT IS

IS IT FUCK! TOM, TELL HIM HOW YOU SPELL STOMACH, WILL YOU
ROGER
TIM
CALM DOWN ROGER. WE'LL ASK GILES. HE'S GOT A DICTIONARY

NO... ACTUALLY HE'S RIGHT ROGER. STOMACH **IS** SPELT S-T-O-M-A-C-H
G

WELL FUCK ME BACKWARDS! YOU LIVE AND LEARN
**CUT!!**

PERHAPS WE SHOULD JUST GO STRAIGHT ON TO THE ANAGRAM ROGER. WE'VE SET UP A NINE LETTER WORD OVER HERE, BUT IT'S BEEN JUMBLED UP!
THE FIRST PERSON TO GUESS WHAT THE WORD IS, WINS!

OH! I SAW THAT EARLIER TOM. IT WAS **FAR** TOO HARD. BUT DON'T WORRY...
I'VE SET A NEW ONE!

MIND YOU, IT'S STILL A **WEE** BIT TRICKY, SO I'M GOING TO GIVE THEM A LITTLE CLUE
CD · GPD · ST

OKAY EVERYONE. YOU **WIPE** THESE BEFORE YOU PULL YOUR TROUSERS UP!
A R S E H L O E S

# IT'S THE PAGE YOU WRITE AND IT'S ALWAYS SHITE

## Advert irony made me laugh

I was driving to work this morning when I saw s sign on the back of a bus. It read, "Are you reading this advertisement? Then so are your customers". I had to laugh, because I sell white sticks and guide dogs to the blind.

N. Walters
London

Whilst digging for treasure, my friend and I were shocked to unearth a dead body, somewhat badly decayed. How we laughed when we suddenly realised we were digging in a cemetary.

M.B.
Edinburgh

## Road to savings

Why oh why don't the government make all the roads straight! That way cars wouldn't need steering wheels and the savings could be passed on to Joe Public.

Joe Public
Grantham

The other day my wife mowed the lawn. Little did she know that I had been watching her from inside the garden shed.

J. Cursiter
Bristol

Are the British public cowards or just plain lazy? The other day, an old lady was attacked in broad daylight in our high street. I stood and watched for a good five minutes during which time not one person lifted a finger to help. Whatever happened to the Dunkirk spirit?

L. Norder
Camberly

I was appalled to read recently that only one in five of our children leave school in the top 20% of the ability range. No wonder this country is heading for third world status. It's time teachers started earning these so-called four figure salaries we hear so much about.

J. Anderson (Dr.)
Dept of Mathmatical Education
Beeston University

Why don't TV companies show fish in aquariums between programmes instead of those expensive adverts. They could put slogans on the glass or on pieces of waxed paper inside the tank.

Nigel Woodhead
London

Aren't dreams incredible. Last night I dreamt I hadn't had a shave and I woke up the next morning to find that it had come true.

James Lowe
Nottingham

## These whales must die

Why is everyone concerned about saving whales? If we don't slaughter them now they'll breed and eat all the available plankton. Consequently, they will develop legs and come onto land in search of alternative food sources. Just think of the damage they'll do in our streets. Are the Greenpeace do-gooders so short sighted that they don't know a **real** threat to the environment when they see one?

J. McConnell
Hemel Hempstead

The other day my wife and I bought our 4 year old son a jigsaw to keep him occupied whilst we went for a picnic. However, when we returned, we found he had managed to plug it in and had cut several of his fingers off.

C. Duckworth
Cheshire

Recently my girlfriend finished with me; saying I was "useless in the trouser department". Ironically enough, the next week I was sacked from my job as head trouser salesman in Marks and Spencers.

C. Perkins
Bristol

## Weekend beer thirst problem

On Saturday nights, it seems I just can't drink enough beer, because every Sunday morning I'm still thirsty.

E.B. Cushion
Worcester

The other day, my wife put the rubbish in the dustbin as she does every day. Little did she know that I had watched every move she made from a small cardboard hide I'd erected by the greenhouse.

J. Cursiter
Bristol

A few nights ago my wife and I were startled by a strange flashing light 200 feet above our heads. Only when my daughter reminded us that we lived in a lighthouse was the mystery solved.

Dr. R.M. Coyle

Amusingly enough, Richard Stilgoe's name is not an anagram of TALENTLESS BASTARD. I have spotted several of these non-anagrams, such as Robert Robinson — POMPOUS PORKER and Anne Diamond — VACANT TART. Can any readers spot anymore?

Roy Harris
Oxford

Last week my wife went shopping with a list written on the back of a bus ticket. She returned later, struggling somewhat, carrying a number 67 bus. She had read the wrong side of the ticket. Do I win £5?

Mr M. Davies
Greater Manchester

## We saw 'punny' side

Whilst watching an hilarious situation comedy, my wife, with tears of mirth in her eyes, mistakenly poured out two glasses of Paraquat instead of our usual beverage. Luckily we both saw the fungicide.

Jon Sendel
Sheffield

The other day I concealed myself in a cupboard above the kettle in our kitchen whilst my wife made a cup of tea. She was completely unaware that I had been watching everything from a small hole I had drilled earlier in the unit.

J. Cursiter
Bristol

## Childhood engine driver ambition realised

It was my childhood ambition to be an engine driver and now I am one.

R.M. Cook MD

I didn't know what to think walking into the kitchen last night finding my wife draped in lasagne and pouring piping hot soup over her head. "I'm putting the dinner on", she quipped. How we laughed on the way to the burns unit.

A. Hampton
Hampton

# TOP TIPS

Stop bread from drying out by keeping it in a bucket of water.
P.J. Ruddock
London

Save petrol by pushing your car to your destination. Invariably, passers by will think you have broken down and help.
S. Pate
Glasgow

Save money on expensive personalised car number plates by simply changing your name to match your existing plate.
Mr KVL 741Y
Lincoln

Save money on doorbell batteries by removing them and going to the door every two minutes to see if anyone is there.
Rod Scott
Leicester

TURN your greenhouse into a garden shed by boarding up the glass windows with wooden planks.
S.T.
Pontefract

AVOID embarrassment after tripping in the street by repeating the same movement several times to make it look like a normal part of your behaviour.
B. Sweeney
Cove Road

SAVE money by taking stitching out of old clothes and using the thread again.
G.T.
Newcastle

When a programme you dislike comes on the TV simply turn down the volume and close your eyes until it is finished.
J. Drallop
Bishop Auckland

Thread a length of string through everything you have in your home. That way, whenever you want to find something, simply follow the string from the beginning and you'll eventually come across it.
E. Tupp
Glamorgan

Turn your garden into a helicopter landing pad by painting a large 'H' in the middle of your lawn using white emulsion paint and a roller.
Paul Sweeney
Kirkham

Fed up with posters falling off walls? Simply file them in a cabinet under P and you'll know where to find them if you want a quick look.
John Kean
Sheffield

SAVE electricity. Turn all your lights out and walk around the house wearing a miner's hat.
D. Purvis
Bolton

BEER poured into washing up liquid changes it from lemon flavour to shandy flavour.
Dave Patterson
Bournemouth

# BOBBIES ON THE BONK!

**Eight out of ten officers in Britain's police force have sex regularly, according to a recent survey. And when they're not out on the beat, the chances are that Britain's bobbies are bonking away at home! "Sex crazed coppers simply can't get enough", said one person yesterday.**

The traditional image of the British bobby, complete with bicycle, is long gone. Nowadays, rather than put their feet up after a hard day on the beat, lusty lawmen head straight for the bedroom. And of all the forces in Britain, the Metropolitan Police are the worst. "More police officers have sex in London than in any other city in Britain", an official told us.

Britain's bobbies - bonking ban?

## SESSIONS

We spoke to one officer's next door neighbour who told us that the perky PC's sex sessions often interupted her TV viewing. "It sometimes goes on all night", she told us. "I don't know how he manages it".

## WORRIED

Senior police chiefs are said to be worried that oversexed officers could come to work exhausted, unfit to carry out their duties. But a spokesman for the Home Office denied that a 'bonking ban' was being considered for all serving officers.

One former police constable who we spoke to admitted having sex with his wife while serving with the Northumbria force, often up to three times a week. He refused to be named, for obvious reasons, and claimed that his saucy frolics **did** effect his work. "At times I'd just be too tired to arrest anyone", he confessed.

## OFFICER

One serving police officer we spoke to was remaining tight lipped about his off-duty antics. 'Piss off", he told us.

# Billy the Fish

FULCHESTER UTD ARE FAVOURITES TO WIN THE CUP FINAL AT WEMBLEY. HOWEVER - THEY SUFFER AN EARLY SETBACK WHEN **BROWN FOX**, THEIR LARGE-BREASTED CHEROKEE WINGER, FORCES A SAVE FROM HER OWN KEEPER: MAN-cum-FISH **BILLY THOMSON**.

WHAT'S WRONG WITH BROWN FOX, BOSS?

WOMEN'S THINGS, SYD. IT'S A GOOD JOB WE'VE GOT A USEFUL SUBSTITUTE ON THE BENCH.

YOU SEE, LIKE MATHEMATICS, FOOTBALL IS A SCIENCE AND THE SAME RULES APPLY TO BOTH. IF MY CALCULATIONS ARE CORRECT, THE DYNAMIC FORCES APPLIED SHOULD SEE THE BALL SAFELY IN THE BACK OF THE NET.

AFTER A FEW INITIAL CALCULATIONS, THE PROF IS QUICKLY ON THE BALL...

GOOD "ON THE BALL" MATHEMATICS FROM THE BALDING ACADEMIC.

BUT, WITH THE GOAL IN HIS SIGHTS...

DÄM UNT BLÄST, ZE BATTERY SHE IS DEAD.

WELL REF, WHAT D'YOU RECKON?

PENALTY TO BARNTON

SURELY A QUESTION-MARK MUST HANG OVER THAT DECISION.

BILLY THOMSON FACES THE MOST IMPORTANT DECISION OF HIS LIFE!

IS BILLY PREPARED TO LAY DOWN HIS LIFE FOR FULCHESTER UNITED?

DON'T MISS THE FINAL EPISODE OF BILLY the FISH IN THE NEXT EPISODE!!

PHOTO LOVE
Mark and Jane, very much in love were setting off on holiday.
OOH, I'M SO LOOKING FORWARD TO OUR HOLIDAY, JANE. THESE PAST TEN YEARS WITH YOU HAVE BEEN THE HAPPIEST OF MY LIFE
I'M LOOKING FORWARD TO IT TOO, SWEETHEART
YOU WAIT HERE BY THIS PHOTO BOOTH WHILE I GO AND GET THE TICKETS
OKAY DARLING! BUT DON'T BE TOO LONG
HELLO, WHAT'S THIS?
IT LOOKS LIKE SOMEONE HAS FORGOTTEN THEIR PHOTOGRAPHS
MY GOD.... BUT SHE'S BEAUTIFUL. I SIMPLY HAVE TO FIND HER!
Shortly.
HERE'S THE TICKETS, MARK. THE TRAIN'S IN. WE CAN GET SRAIGHT ON

NO, JANE. I CAN'T GO. IT'S ALL OVER BETWEEN US
WHAT!?!
I'VE FOUND SOMEONE ELSE WHILE YOU WERE GETTING THE TICKETS

WHO?
I DON'T KNOW WHO SHE IS OR WHERE SHE IS. I ONLY KNOW I LOVE HER AND I WANT TO SPEND THE REST OF MY LIFE WITH HER. AND THAT'S ENOUGH!

So.
WELL, IF THAT'S WHAT YOU REALLY WANT, I CAN'T STOP YOU! GOODBYE

GPD CD 9.88 Photography by Colin Davison

Shot using Kodak Romantichrome 100

BIG VERN'S
CHRISTMAS CAPER

I'M TAKING MY YOUNG NEPHEW MARTIN OUT TO DO A BIT OF CHRISTMAS SHOPPING, VERN.
DO YOU WANT TO COME ALONG?

FORGET IT ERNIE. IT'S A MUG'S GAME. I'M STRICTLY ON THE STRAIGHT AND NARRA. I'M NOT GETTING MY HANDS DIRTY ON THIS ONE.
BUT VERN. MARTIN AND I ARE ONLY NIPPING TO THE SHOPS!

I DON'T LIKE IT ERNIE. THE KID LOOKS GREEN - HE COULD BLOW IT. YOU KNOW I ONLY WORK WITH PROS.
SUN
OH, COME ON VERN; WE'RE ONLY GOING SHOPPING.

A SHOP EH? SOUNDS TASTY. COME ON- SIT DOWN AND TELL ME ABOUT THE PLAN.

WELL, THE PLAN IS THAT WE'RE GOING SHOPPING... THAT'S ALL,
WE'LL BROWSE AROUND AND BUY A FEW PRESENTS. MARTIN PARTICULARLY WANTS TO SEE THE TOY DEPARTMENT.

OKAY. SO THIS IS THE SHOP, RIGHT. WE ARRIVE HERE. THEN WHAT?
WELL... WE ARRIVE... DO OUR SHOPPING... THEN LEAVE. IT SHOULD ONLY TAKE US A COUPLE OF HOURS.

IT'S TOO LONG ERNIE, TOO LONG. WHEN WE HIT THE SHOP, WE GOTTA BE OUT IN 2 MINUTES, THAT'S ALL. NO SLIP-UPS.
WELL, WE CAN TRY TO BE QUICKER... BUT THERE'S A FEW THINGS I WANT TO BUY.

LOOK VERN, IT'S GETTING LATE NOW, SO CAN YOU DECIDE WHETHER YOU'RE COMING OR NOT?

OKAY ERNIE. YOU CAN COUNT ME IN.
RIGHT
WELL... WE'D BETTER GET OFF THEN.

ER... YOU WON'T NEED THAT, VERN... WE'RE ONLY DOING A BIT OF SHOPPING, REMEMBER?
INSURANCE, ERNIE. A BIT OF INSURANCE IN CASE THINGS GO WRONG!

SOON...
AFTER THIS JOB ERNIE, THAT'S IT. I'M QUITTING. I'M GUNNU SET MESELF UP. GET A NICE LITTLE PLACE IN SPAIN.
THAT SOUNDS LOVELY, VERN.

AT THE SHOPS...
WE'RE GOING IN HERE, VERN. ARE YOU COMING WITH US?
TOY SHOP
I DON'T LIKE IT, ERNIE. IT DOESN'T SMELL RIGHT.

OH COME ON VERN. YOU'RE BEING RIDICULOUS.
CAN I SEE THE TOY GUNS UNCLE ERNIE?
OF COURSE YOU CAN, MARTIN.

INSIDE...
LOOK, THIS IS A NICE ONE MARTIN.
WATER PISTOLS
ERNIE!

THE BROAD BEHIND THE COUNTER, SHE'S MADE ME. COME ON - WE'VE GOT TO GET OUT OF HERE.
CAN I SEE THAT ONE?
CERTAINLY.
CALM DOWN, VERN. WE'LL BE LEAVING SOON.

LOOK OUT ERNIE!! SHE'S GOT A GUN!!
K-BOOF
BAM!
AAAGH!

COME ON! LET'S SCARPER BEFORE THE FILTH ARRIVES!
WE'RE NOT GOING ANYWHERE! FOR GOD'S SAKE, VERN! YOU'VE SHOT HER!

IN THAT CASE I'M SORRY ERNIE. I CAN'T LEAVE YOU TWO HERE TO SING LIKE CANARIES!
?

OOOH.
YAAGH!
BLAM!
BLAM!
AND NO BASTARD COPPER'S GONNA TAKE **ME** ALIVE!
BAM!

An amazing behind the scenes look at British Intellige

# MY NAME IS JOHNSON... ...REG JOHNSON

EXCLUSIVE

**When we think of secret agents we think of James Bond, 007, of fast cars, action and beautiful women. But what is it really like being a spy? Is it as exciting and glamorous as the movies would have us believe?**

Until recently Reg Johnson was an undercover operative working for British Intelligence. But now he is blowing the lid off Britain's secret service in a book which makes 'Spycatcher' look like a kid's bedtime story. And here, in an exclusive serialisation of his book, Reg dispells the myth that the Bond films have created and replaces fiction with fact in the first TRUE story of the British Secret Service.

**Extracts from the book that makes Spycatcher look not very controversial**

'When I watch a James Bond movie I can't help laughing. In real life the secret service is nothing like that. We do most of our work behind a desk, without a gun in sight.

### UNDERGROUND

The hardest part of working for the secret service is getting the job in the first place. I was half an hour late for my interview 'cos I couldn't find the office. I had to go into a phone box somewhere in London and dial a secret number. Then the phone box turned into a lift and went down to the British Intelligence Secret Headquarters, which is underground. Of course I couldn't find the right phone box, and when I did there was a queue of people waiting to use it.

### SHARKS

The interview itself was tough. I thought I was doing quite well, then somebody pressed a button and my chair fell backwards tipping me into a pool full of sharks. It was all part of the interview. I had to kill the sharks and escape. Luckily I killed them all, and they asked me to start on Monday. But there was at least a dozen other blokes who weren't so lucky!

Once you're in you get several days of special training before they send you on any missions. Mind you, there's none of those fancy gadgets that 'Q' comes up with in the movies. That stuff is pure nonsense. In reality they just teach you basic things like fighting and how to escape from places. You get flying lessons too — in planes and helicopters — and they teach you how to drive a car — on two wheels, and under water.

### EXOTIC

After training they give you a gun and a car and send you on a special misson. Any old car won't do. It has to be bullet proof and have an ejector seat. After you've been a spy for two years they give you a car that turns into an aeroplane.

The kind of work done by the secret service is far removed from the excitement and glamour of the movies. In James Bond the villians live on exotic islands surrounded by beautiful women. But in real life it's nothing like that.

### BIKINI

I only ever got sent to an island once. A Russian spy had stolen an atom bomb and was going to destroy the world. When I got there I found his girlfriend on the beach wearing a bikini. We had sex, then she helped me to find the bomb and diffuse it. If we had been two seconds later it would have gone off. That was a close shave, even by my standards.

### TEETH

Being a spy is a dangerous job. One day I was on top of a cable car when I was attacked by a tall man with metal teeth. We had a fight and I knocked him off. Then I managed to climb up the wire all the way to the top just before the cable car exploded. Of course I got paid danger money for that sort of thing. On a really dangerous mission I could come out with £200 a week, including overtime and danger money. Of course, there were other benefits too.

### KARATE

Spies always have to have sex with women, usually to get secret information out of them, or to get them to help you escape from places. Once I was in Hong Kong when six women in bikinis who were good at karate attacked me. Luckily I'm a black belt in karate, so I won. Then I had sex with them. Afterwards they gave me all the secret information and then helped me to escape.

### WARDROBE

You can never relax being a spy. Even at weekends. Every time you enter a room you have to check to see if someone's hiding behind the door, or in a wardrobe. Once I was going to town on a bus when a fat Chinese man tried to kill me with a sharp metal hat. I had to kill him with some electrical wires and throw him out of the window. I managed to get off the bus just before it exploded.

### QUEEN

It's no fun killing people, but when you're a spy you have to. But first you have to have a licence to kill. And they're a lot harder to get then T.V. licenses, I can tell you. Your application form has to be signed by the Queen of England, and they cost £500 a year. That might seem like a lot of money, but being a spy I couldn't do without it.

Next week: How I had to escape from the moon after being drugged and put in a space rocket by another spy with three nipples and a golden gun.'

'I WAS A SPY, HONEST' by Reg Johnson, is published by Omlette Books, price £2.95.

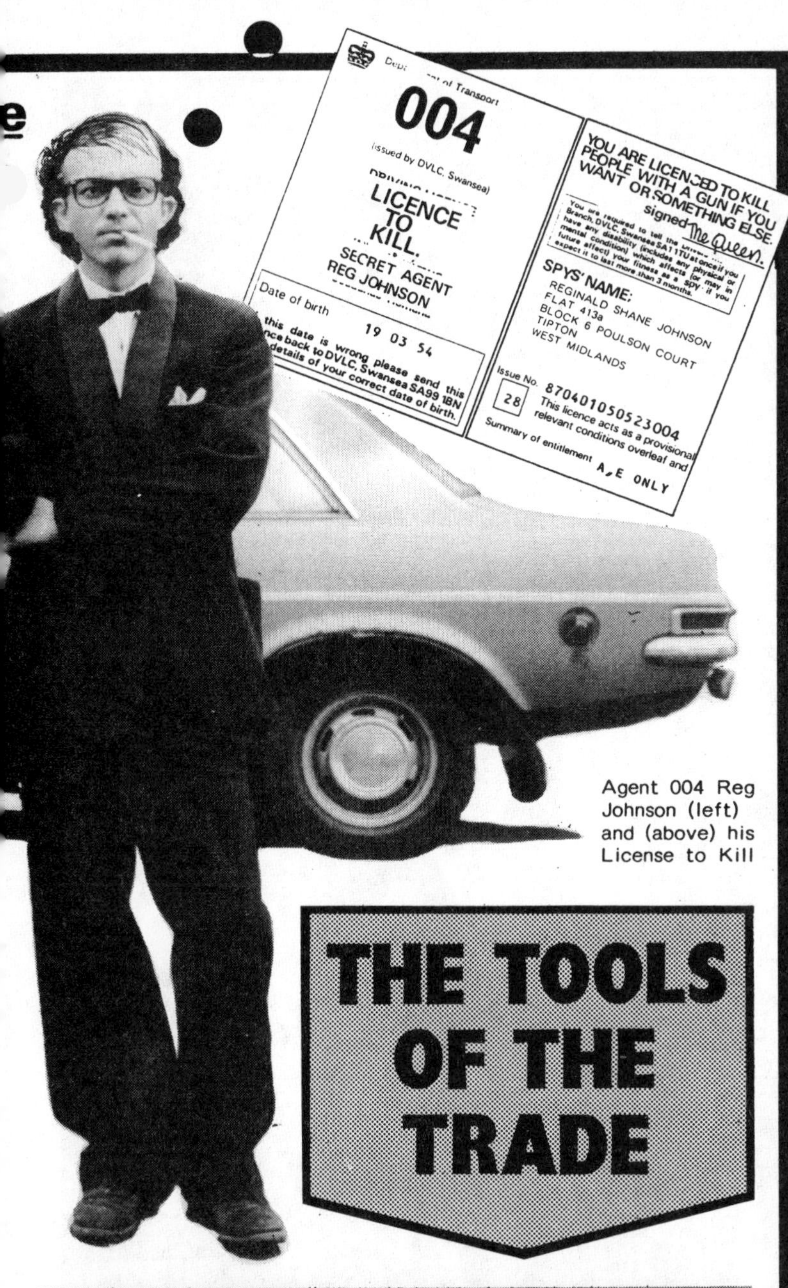
Department of Transport
004
(issued by DVLC, Swansea)
LICENCE TO KILL.
SECRET AGENT
REG JOHNSON
Date of birth 19 03 54
this date is wrong please send this ...nce back to DVLC, Swansea SA99 1BN ...details of your correct date of birth.

YOU ARE LICENCED TO KILL PEOPLE WITH A GUN IF YOU WANT OR SOMETHING ELSE.
signed The Queen.

You are required to tell the Drivers ... Branch, DVLC, Swansea SA1 1TU at once if you have any disability (includes any physical or mental condition) which affects (or may in future affect) your fitness as a spy if you expect it to last more than 3 months.

SPYS' NAME:
REGINALD SHANE JOHNSON
FLAT 413a
BLOCK 6 POULSON COURT
TIPTON
WEST MIDLANDS

Issue No. 28 870401050523004
This licence acts as a provisional relevant conditions overleaf and
Summary of entitlement A, E ONLY

Agent 004 Reg Johnson (left) and (above) his License to Kill

## THE TOOLS OF THE TRADE

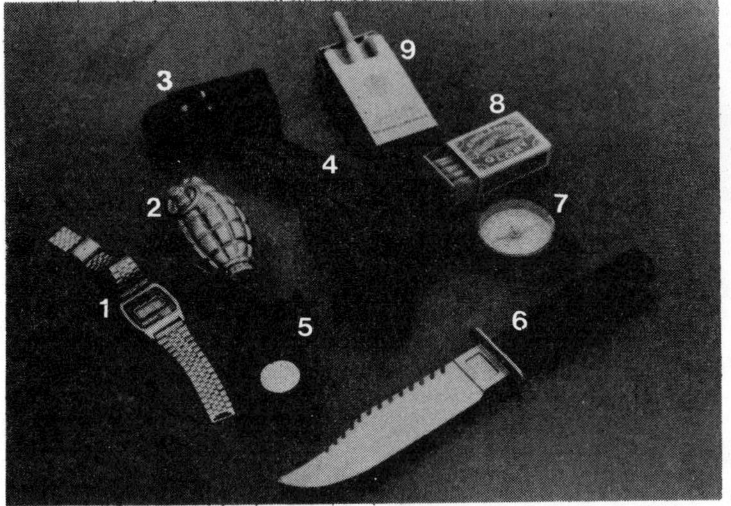


Here is just a small selection of some of the equipment used by Reg Johnson on his secret missions. (1) A special watch which tells the time underwater and even in space. (2) Hand Grenade (3) Exploding camera. (4) Special gun which turns into a cigarette lighter when you press a button. (5) Walky talky radio for sending messages back to base. (6) Knife with road maps, emergency food supplies and waterproof clothing inside the handle. (7) Special spy compass. (8) Exploding matches. (9) Cigarette packet missile launcher. Each cigarette is a missile in disguise, powerful enough to blow up ten helicopters.

# McCARTNEY 'STOLE MILK'

## Greedy ex-Beatle pinched pensioner's pintas

**The pop world has been rocked to its foundations by amazing allegations that millionaire superstar Paul McCartney — one of the wealthiest men in Britain — has been STEALING milk from the doorsteps of an elderly neighbour near his luxury home on the Mull of Kintyre, Scotland.**

And furious local resident Mrs Isla McKitterick believes the greedy ex-Beatle could have **MADE OFF** with literally **GALLONS** of milk since his crime wave began several months ago. She believes that McCartney launches regular 'dawn raids' on her doorstep from his converted farmhouse only 8 miles away, and then returns home to **GUZZLE** the stolen milk with his wife Linda and their two children.

### PRISON

"This has been going on for some time now", Mrs McKitterick told us. "I've reported it to the police, but they still haven't done a thing about it. They know where he lives — I think they should go up there and arrest him. He should be sent to prison".

### EVIDENCE

However, local police are powerless to act against the wealthy star due to lack of evidence. "There is no evidence whatsoever to support these allegations", we were told.

### THEFTS

Meanwhile a spokesman for the 40 year old star denied all knowledge of the thefts, and dismissed the claims as "ridiculous".

Mrs McKitterick is no stranger to controversy. She last made the headlines in 1974 when she accused the late Elvis Presley of intercepting her mail and opening letters which had been addressed to her.

Fellas! If you are thinking of having sex with a fish, then you're out of luck, according to one leading expert on marine biology. (That's fish to you and me).

For he tells us that fish are not attracted to men in the same way that women are.

### LIVE

"Fish are completely different to women", our expert told us. "They live underwater, and have an entirely incompatible system of reproduction". In other words it's strictly "no sex please, we're fish!"

Jack Black
and his dog
Silver
in THE
CHRISTMAS
TREE MYSTERY

The Christmas holidays were here at last, and young Jack Black and his dog Silver were staying at Aunt Meg's log cabin in a Scottish pine forest.

One day, Jack and Silver went out for a walk in the forest.
COME ON SILVER. LAST ONE TO THAT TREE IS A SQUASHED TOMATO.

But....
WHOA!

Jack clambered to his feet and looked to see what had tripped him up.
THAT'S ODD. I WONDER WHAT IT IS? I'D BETTER GO AND FETCH THE POLICE.

Shortly....
WHAT IS IT, P.C. McBARNETT?
WELL JACK, IT LOOKS LIKE A TREE STUMP, BUT I DON'T KNOW WHAT HAPPENED TO THE TREE. FRANKLY, I'M BAFFLED.

Jack too was puzzled, and as he and Silver walked home, he wondered what could have happened to the tree. Suddenly, he noticed thick smoke coming from the centre of the forest.
HMM. THAT'S ODD!

Jack and Silver traced the smoke to a small cottage deep in the forest.
GOSH! A COTTAGE! WE'D BETTER TAKE A CLOSER LOOK.

They both crept stealthily towards the cottage and peered into the window.
SILVER, LOOK AT THIS!

Jack could hardly believe his eyes. Inside he saw Mr McDougall, the poor cobbler and his wife keeping warm in front of a roaring log fire. It all began to make sense. Jack was convinced that the wood on the fire came from the missing tree.

Back home, Jack explained all about the tree to Aunt Meg.
WELL, MR AND MRS McDOUGALL ARE VERY POOR JACK. I'M SURE THEY ONLY TOOK WHAT THEY NEEDED TO KEEP WARM.
BUT YOU'RE MISSING THE POINT, AUNT MEG. HE'S STOLEN THAT TREE, AND HE MUST BE MADE TO PAY FOR HIS CRIME.

Jack knew that one tree would not burn for ever and soon, Mr McDougall would cut down another.
COME ON, SILVER.
The next morning, he and Silver set off to catch McDougall red handed.

And sure enough, they soon found him cutting down another tree. Jack knew he had to act.
GOSH!

STOP RIGHT THERE, YOU BAD MAN.

McDougall took to his heels in fright and Jack gave chase, but as he did, the tree came crashing down on top of him.
OH NO!

The tree lay across Jack's legs and pinned him firmly to the ground. There was only one hope.
QUICK, SILVER. GO TO THE VILLAGE AND FETCH P.C. MCBARNETT.

Silver understood perfectly and raced through the forest and over the hillside as fast as his legs could carry him.

P.C. McBarnett was on patrol in the village.
HELLO THERE SILVER..... WHY, WHERE'S YOUNG JACK? IS HE IN TROUBLE?

WOOF!
The local bobby knew something was wrong, and with Silver leading the way he was soon heading for the scene of the crime in a fast car.

GNNN!
After being rescued, Jack explained to P.C. McBarnett how McDougall had been stealing wood. Shortly they arrived at the cobbler's cottage where the brave bobby broke down the door.

Jack heard a door bang at the back of the cottage and looked around to see the old cobbler making good his escape.

But Jack had planned ahead and old McDougall was caught fast in one of the bear traps the young detective had set earlier that morning.
ARRRRRGH!

COME ON. YOU'LL NOT BE CUTTING ANY TREES DOWN FOR A LONG TIME. JUST BREAKING ROCKS!
P.C. McBarnett frogmarched the crook back to the car.

Shortly....
BUT WHAT ABOUT POOR MRS MCDOUGALL. SHE'S TOO OLD TO LOOK AFTER HERSELF. CAN SHE STAY WITH AUNT MEG AND ME OVER CHRISTMAS?
NO JACK. SHE'S ALREADY BEING TAKEN TO A SECURE INSTITUTION FOR THE OLD AND BEWILDERED.

Later, Jack decorated the tree that had earlier kept him prisoner.
WASN'T IT NICE OF P.C. MCBARNETT TO LET YOU KEEP THE TREE, JACK? WE'LL HAVE A VERY MERRY CHRISTMAS NOW.

# 20 THINGS YOU NEVER KNEW ABOUT HOUSES

**An Englishman's house is his castle, or so the saying goes. And let's face it, in Britain today we've all gone house buying bonkers! Whether it's a semi in Sunderland, a mid-terrace in Mid Lothian or a flat in Flamborough, we all want to own our own home.**

Nowadays nine out of ten per cent more people own their own homes than they did previously. And it's a figure that's growing. But as we spend more and more money on property, do we know what we're buying? How much do we **really** know about houses? For instance, did you know ...

**1** When the Queen and Prince Phillip bought their first house, Buckingham Palace, in 1948 they paid around £2,500. If they were to sell it today it would probably fetch a staggering £10 million — or more if they left the carpets.

**2** Rising house prices are nothing new. When Stonehenge was originally built it probably cost its owners no more than a few shillings in cave man money. When we rang the National Trust yesterday and asked them how much it was now worth, they told us it was not for sale.

**3** The average house contains 32,400 bricks — enough to make 54 small coal bunkers, just over 38 outside lavatories, 6 garages or 2 houses half as big as the first one.

**4** Not all houses are made of bricks. Some are made of timber, others wood. And believe it or not, in the fairy tale of the same name, Hansel and Gretel found a house that was made out of gingerbread.

**5** If you went into an estate agents in Iceland and asked for a house, you'd be in for a big surprise. Because people in Iceland live in igloos, a kind of circular house made out of snow.

**6** If you are buying a house, get to know the people you're buying it from. There will be many things to discuss, and being on good terms with them will help things run more smoothly. Organise day trips together, or perhaps a weekend in the country. Or if you're going to the cinema, why not give them a ring and ask them if they's like to come.

**7** House music — music that is about houses — first appeared in the early eighties when Shakin' Stevens wrote his smash hit 'This 'Ole House'. Stevens later went on to record another hit record, 'Green Door' which was about the front door of his house.

**8** If the barman tells you your drink is "on the house", don't worry. You won't need a ladder to reach it. 'On the house' is simply an expression meaning that you do not have to pay.

**9** There have been many TV programmes with the word 'house' in them. These include 'On The House', 'Bless This House' and 'Man About The House'.

**10** And 'Little House On The Prairie'.

**11** Going home at night must be very confusing for TV celebrity Bob Monkhouse. For the 60 year old comedian has no less than **three** different houses to choose from. He lives in one, another is his television programme 'Bob's Full House', and the third one is part of his surname.

**12** If you talk about houses in a bingo hall, the chances are that someone will give you a prize. That's because in bingo the word 'house' means that you have won.

**13** Greenhouses are not green as their name suggests. And they're not houses either. They are in fact small glass sheds used for growing vegetables.

**14** Everyone has heard of The Housemartins, but did you know that there are two types? One is a pop group from Hull, the other a small bird which nests under the eves of a house. And there are also people who live in houses called Martin, as well.

**15** So that means there are three.

**16** The smallest house in the world was built in Massachusetts, U.S.A. in 1811 for the world's smallest man, Calvin Phillips. However the house, which was less than one foot high and had a front door no bigger than a playing card, was so small that even Mr Phillips did not fit in it, and he died a year later.

**17** Try running up the stairs in a bungalow and you'll fall flat on your face. That's because a bungalow is a special house without any stairs.

**18** No matter where you place a snail, it will always find its way home. That's because snails carry their homes on their backs! Even the world's strongest man, Geoff Capes, could not match that feat. In fact he couldn't even carry his bathroom for very long without falling over.

**19** Like many animals, African Elephants do not live in houses. They just live in the street.

**A house**

**20** Humans and cuckoos are unique within the animal kingdom, because neither of them build their own homes. Cuckoos break into other birds nests while they're out and lay their eggs on the floor. Humans simply call in the builders.

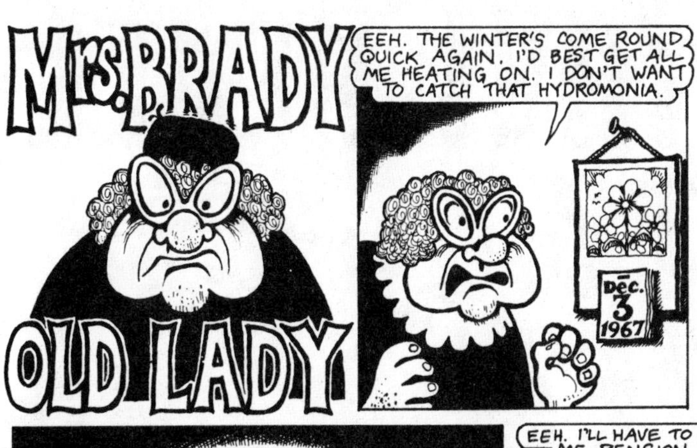
Mrs. BRADY
OLD LADY
EEH. THE WINTER'S COME ROUND QUICK AGAIN. I'D BEST GET ALL ME HEATING ON. I DON'T WANT TO CATCH THAT HYDROMONIA.
DEC. 3 1967

MIND YOU, NOBODY WOULD CARE IF I DID. THEY NEVER COME TO SEE ME.

BRRR. LOOK AT IT OUT THERE. I'M GLAD I'M INDOORS.

...AND IN THE HOTTEST JULY SINCE RECORDS BEGAN...
MIND YOU, THIS LOT WON'T KEEP ME WARM. AND THEY'LL EXPECT ME TO PAY FOR IT.

EEH. I'LL HAVE TO GO OUT AND FETCH ME PENSION IN THIS WEATHER AND ALL.
WHEN I WAS A LITTLE BOY, THEY'D BRING ME PENSION ROUND BECAUSE ALL THE SOLDIERS ON THE FRONT HAD THE REAL EGGS. AND THERE WERE NO BANANAS.

OI! YOU TWO MAKE YOURSELVES USEFUL. CLEAR THE SNOW OFF MY PATH INSTEAD OF STANDING AROUND DOING NOTHING AND VANDALISING PHONE BOXES.
?
VAL-U-LIKE

I'LL PICK UP ME CHRISTMAS BONUS WHILE I'M AT IT. I DON'T KNOW HOW MUCH IT IS BUT IT SHOULD BE AT LEAST TWICE THAT. IT'S AN INSULT.
POST OFFICE
BARGAINS 'R' US

EEH. I'VE GOT TO QUEUE FOR IT TOO. IT'S DEGRADING. WELL I'M NOT GOING TO WAIT FOR EVER.
OPEN
OPEN
OPEN
OPEN
OPEN
BARGAINS 'R' US

CAN I HELP YOU MRS. BRADY?
OPEN
OPEN
OPEN
OPEN
THEY MUST THINK I'VE GOT ALL DAY.
BARGAINS 'R' US

YES MRS. BRADY. IS IT YOUR PENSION?
ABOUT TIME TOO. AND LESS OF YOUR CHEEK IF YOU DON'T MIND YOUNG MAN. YOU'RE NOT SO OLD AS I CAN'T PUT YOU ACROSS MY KNEE.

GIVE THESE A SERVICE WASH. PUT SOME ELBOW GREASE INTO IT THIS TIME. AND I WANT ALL THE BUTTONS BACK. SO USE PLENTY OF CARBOLIC.
BARGAINS 'R' US

TAKE THESE ALONG TO THE FLORISTS WILL YOU. SHE'LL PROBABLY PICK THEM UP THERE TOMORROW.
OPEN
OPEN

I MUST GET MESELF SOME OF THEM FLEECE-LINED BOOTS. YOU KNOW. THE ONES WITH THE ZIPS ON. I HAVEN'T GOT ANY OF THOSE.

MIND - I WANT THE CHUNKY ZIPS. I CAN'T GET ME FINGERS ROUND THEM DAFT FIDDLY ONES. I GET ALL ORTHOPAEDIC IN ME FINGERS IN THIS FROSTY WEATHER. OOOH. IT'S BITTER.

HERE. JUST FEEL THAT. ME KNUCKLES ARE LIKE BLOCKS OF ICE, AREN'T THEY?

LATER...
FAMOUS ARMY S

CACKLE! NOBODY BEATS ADA BRADY TO THE JANUARY SALES. I'VE HAD ME EYE ON A NEW HAT FOR AGES.
ACE BUILDER'S MERCHANTS TRADE ONLY
WE HAVE MOVED!
I MIGHT EVEN GET ON THE TELLY.

ARE YOU COMING WITH US FOR A NICE CUP OF TEA DEAR?
EEEH. IT'S THAT NICE JUDITH CHALMERS LOOK.
ACE
TWILIGHT PASTURES TOP SECURITY REST HOME
GPD. SD. ST. 10.88

# UFO's — DO THEY REALLY EXIST OR IS IT JUST A LOAD OF SHITE?

**UFO's — do they really exist, or are they just figments of our vivid imaginations? Every year there are literally thousands of reported sightings of unidentified flying objects over Britain alone. But can they be taken seriously? Is there REALLY someone out there watching us? Have life forms from another planet visited the Earth? Every day more and more evidence seems to suggest that they have.**

However, the experts are divided. Some say that UFO's exist. Others say they don't. Some aren't really sure. But whatever your opinion, you simply cannot ignore the evidence.

## T.V. star kidnapped by aliens

### MAN

UFOs are a phenomenon which affect not only ordinary people, but TV celebrities as well. And one man who should know more than most about the existence of 'visitors' from other planets is funny man BOB MONKHOUSE. For 60-year-old Bob is one of the few people to have survived a UFO 'kidnapping.'

### SHOT

Bob's ordeal began in 1973 at the time when he was hosting ITV's popular game show *'The Golden Shot'*. Driving home from work late one night he decided to take a short cut across an isolated moor in North Yorkshire, and got lost. Suddenly several bright lights appeared in the sky above his car and the well known comedian and all-round entertainer slowly began to lose consciousness. When he awoke several hours later Bob was still in his car, parked in exactly the same spot, but on the seat next to him was a briefcase containing £750.

### FEE

Experts who later examined him believe that Monkhouse was the victim of a bizarre UFO kidnapping, and that he had been taken on board an alien space ship to entertain the crew. The money had been left to cover his fee for the evening. Police traced the bank notes and discovered that they had been part of a consignment of money which had gone missing in the Bermuda triangle several years earlier.

How well the comic's act went down with his alien audience we may never know, for Bob's memory of the entire incident was erased by his captors, and his brain was specially programmed to deny that it ever happened.

## Late night visit costs Bob a bomb

One man will never forget the night he came face to face with an alien. For the incident haunts him to this very day.

### WINDOW

Bus driver Bob McPherson of Motherwell was awoken one morning at 4am by a loud 'bang'. He peered out of the window and to his astonishment saw a bright silver saucer-shaped object, about six feet in diameter, lying half buried in his garden.

### KITCHEN

"I immediately ran downstairs to see what had happened, but when I got to the kitchen door I was suddenly frozen by some strange force. I couldn't move a muscle." Bob looked on as the side of the UFO opened, and a shadowy figure emerged. According to Bob it was a small, human-like creature, measuring less than 2 feet tall.

Bob - late night visit cost him a bomb

"I stood and watched as it walked past me into my house, carrying some kind of strange cable or tube which it plugged into a wall socket in the kitchen. Then there was a loud humming noise which went on for about 30 seconds until the space ship began to glow brightly." At this point the alien returned to his space ship and the door closed.

### SETTEE

"I ran upstairs to fetch my camera. But I got back just in time to see the UFO rising up at incredible speed and then shooting off across the sky," said Bob.

### LOUNGE

He didn't manage to get a photograph, but Bob was left with something else to remind him of the visit — an electricity bill for £375.36 which arrived the next day! When Bob tried to explain what had happened to the Electricity Board, they were sceptical to say the least. "They've told me that I have to pay off the whole amount in weekly instalments," he told us.

Will Bob ever be repaid for his hospitality? Or was he the victim of a new breed of criminal — thieves from space? Perhaps we will never know . . . . .

## T.V. soap stars live in terror

For several months an alien space ship paid regular visits to the set of the hit BBC TV soap 'EastEnders.' For a randy space romeo on board the vessel had developed a 'crush' on actress Anita Dobson.

### CAST

The cast of the show were sworn to secrecy by TV chiefs who feared that any bad publicity would affect viewing figures. However, Miss Dobson, who played sexy pub landlady Angie Watts in the series, eventually threatened to call police after the captain of the space ship got drunk on space beer and made improper suggestions to her.

### BOSSES

Bosses at the Beeb forced the actress to quit, and the 'visits' ceased shortly afterwards. The entire 'EastEnders' cast, including Miss Dobson, remain sworn to secrecy.

# EXIST

# HOLLYWOOD SPACE HORROR

## F.B.I. murdered Monroe in Whitehouse cover-up

Monroe - space murder?

**A growing number of experts are now taking seriously the theory that aliens may have already landed on Earth and could be living among us disguised in human form. And far fetched though it may sound, there is striking evidence to support this theory.**

How can UFO's be explained? 'It's a mystery to me' says Shakin' Stevens, as a flying saucer circles the Houses of Parliament.

Lavatory attendant Brian Wilkinson believes that glamorous film star Marilyn Monroe was murdered by the FBI because she knew about space aliens working inside the Whitehouse. But Brian, 42, wasn't prepared to tell us for fear that he too may be killed.

### PUB

And unemployed bricklayer Walter Purviss believes he has identified visiting aliens in his home town of Huddersfield, and claims to have confronted a group of them as they sat drinking quietly in a pub near his home.

"I walked into the pub and noticed these three sitting in the corner. There was something eerie about them, so I followed one of them into the toilet. I made no bones about it. I simply asked him whether he was an alien or not. He obviously was because he punched me in the face then walked off."

### COVER

By the time Mr Purviss recovered, the aliens, realising their cover was blown, had left. "It's just as well," he told us. "Cos if I ever see them again I'm gonna give them a bloody good hiding."

Have aliens already landed? Are they living among us? Can you trust your neighbour? Perhaps even your husband or wife are 'visitors' in disguise. We may never know . . . . .

# THE GREAT UFO DEBATE
# WHAT THE STARS SAY

**If aliens did land on Earth, what would they look like? That's the question we put to a few top celebrities, and this is what they said.**

**MARTI PELLOW, sexy lead singer with Wet, Wet, Wet told us that aliens would probably be green skinned, wiry creatures with six legs and long, lizard-like tongues. "They'd use their tongues to catch space insects," says Marti.**

**Bros star LUKE GOSS believes that aliens will be like humans, but bald and with silver eyes. "They'll wear silver space suits and have a ray gun in the middle of their forehead," he added.**

**Brother MATT disagreed. "I don't think you'll be able to see aliens," he explained. "They'll be sort of invisible, like a cloud of gas," he told us.**

**Radio One DJ ANNE NIGHTINGALE took time off from her lively Sunday night request show to tell us what she thought aliens would look like. "They'll probably walk on two legs, like we do, but they'll have huge, long necks, like dinosaurs, and eight arms, all with suckers on the end," she told us. "And they'll be purple," she added.**

**GYLES BRANDRETH won't hang about to see what the aliens look like if he sees a UFO land. He'll run for his life! "I've got a terrible feeling that aliens will be like giant snails with big antennae, and enormous metal teeth," he confessed.**

**Have you ever spotted a UFO? Perhaps you have come face to face with aliens from another planet. If so, this could be your chance to win a fabulous prize. Because we're giving away 500 Mars Bars to the winner of this exciting UFO competition. And there's a Milky Way for each of the ten runners up. All you have to do to enter is write and tell us about your UFO experience. Entries should be no longer than 500 words, and MUST be accompanied by a photograph.**

### PHOTOS

**Send your eye-witness accounts together with photographs, to Viz UFO Competition, PO Box 1PT, Newcastle upon Tyne NE99 1PT. All entries must arrive by 31st December 1988. Photographs can only be returned if accompanied by a stamped addressed envelope. The winner will be the entry which we decide has won.**

Sally Rushton had been going steady with motor cycle despatch rider Andre West for almost a year - a year spent tortured over the fear that one day Andre would be involved in a serious accident.

Later, Sally returned to work.

LOOK, WHY DON'T YOU TAKE THE REST OF THE DAY OFF WORK. I'M SURE YOUR BOSS WON'T MIND. YOU TALK IT OVER WITH YOUR BOYFRIEND TONIGHT
YES... YES, I WILL. THANK YOU
At home.
I'LL TALK TO HIM AS SOON AS HE GETS HERE, I'LL ASK HIM TO PACK THAT JOB IN BEFORE IT DRIVES ME INSANE
OH DEAR, HE'S LATE. I'D BETTER PHONE THE OFFICE TO SEE IF HE'S OKAY
HELLO.... CAN I SPEAK TO ANDRE, PLEASE?
ANDRE? OH, HAVEN'T YOU HEARD? ANDRE WAS KILLED OUTRIGHT IN AN HORRIFIC ROAD ACCIDENT THIS AFTERNOON. EEH! YOU SHOULD HAVE SEEN IT. THERE WAS BLOOD EVERYWHERE. IT FAIR TURNED MY STOMACH
OH. GOD! NO
Sally was stunned. Her worst nightmare had come true.
YOU FOOL, ANDRE, YOU DAMNED FOOL
The doorbell rang.
I BET THAT'S THE POLICE
THEY'LL PROBABLY WANT ME TO IDENTIFY THE BODY

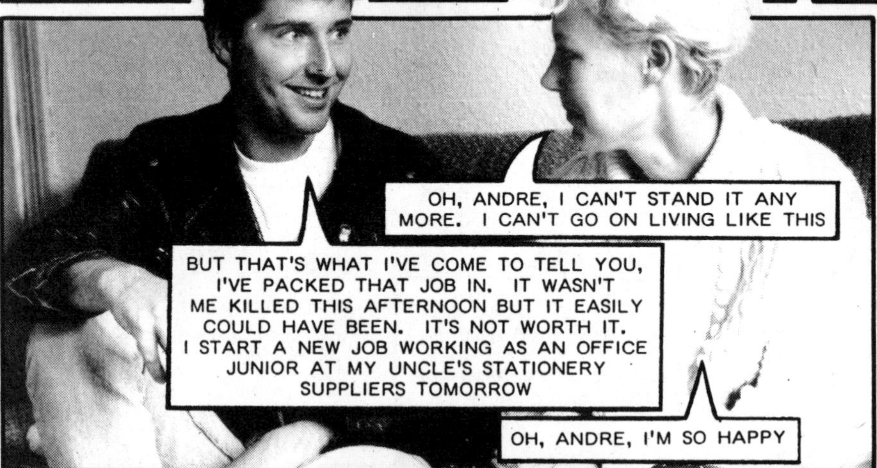

GPD CD 9.88 Photography by Colin Davison

LEADING BY A GOAL TO NIL, FULCHESTER UNITED LOOK ALL SET TO WIN THE CUP FINAL UNTIL A LAST MINUTE PENALTY IS AWARDED AGAINST THEM. AND WITH A FORTY POUND BOMB ATTACHED TO THE BALL, ANY ATTEMPT TO SAVE THE KICK WILL MEAN INSTANT DEATH FOR FULCHESTER'S BRILLIANT "FISH-LIKE" GOALKEEPER BILLY THOMSON.

A DEATHLY HUSH DESCENDS ON WEMBLEY STADIUM AS THE KICK IS ABOUT TO BE TAKEN...

DON'T MISS THE NEXT THRILLING EPISODE ON PAGE 38!

FREE! Viz

# A super sexational pop gift to cut out and keep

# NudiScope™

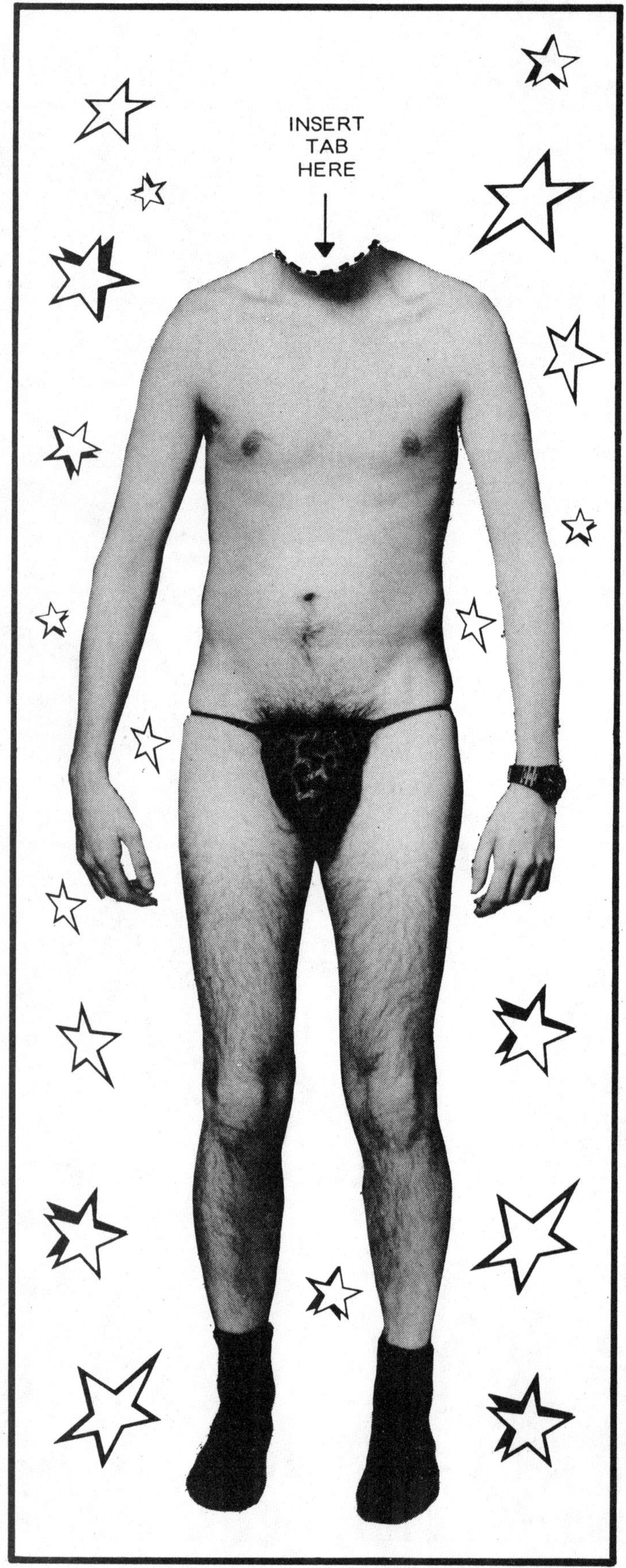


**GIRLS! Have you ever wondered what it would be like to see Shakey starkers or Bros in their birthday suits?**

**We all know pop stars are sexy with their clothes on, so just think how much sexier they would be in the altogether.**

**Well, now you can stop wondering and find out for real, with your fantastic free NudiScope™ the gift which lets your wildest dreams come true. Simply follow the instructions and see if your favourite BIG stars live up to your expectations.**

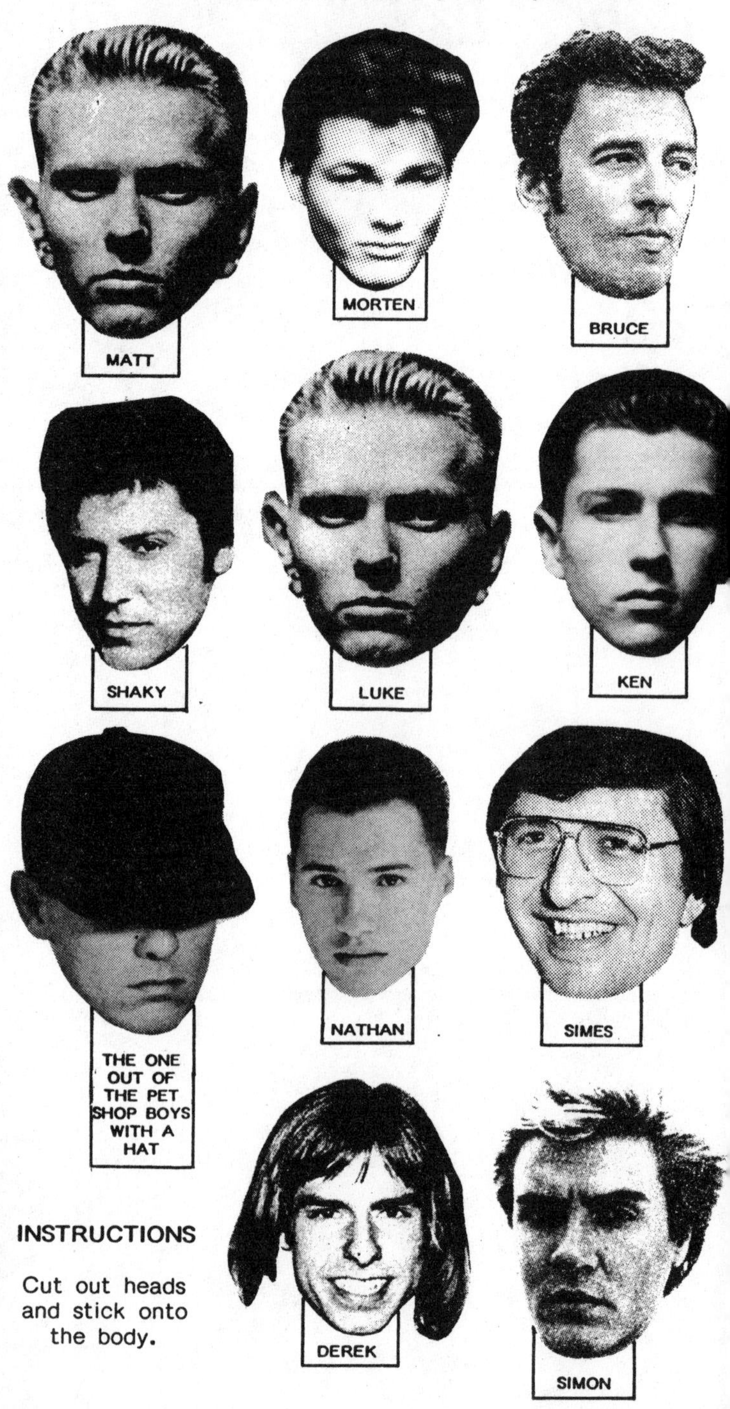


**INSTRUCTIONS**

Cut out heads and stick onto the body.

FINBARR SAUNDERS And his DOUBLE ENTENDRES

FINBARR & HIS MOTHER ARE DOING SOME LAST-MINUTE XMAS SHOPPING
THERE'S JUST TIME FOR A VISIT TO SANTA'S GROTTO, FINBARR. DO YOU FANCY IT?

SO...
WELL LITTLE MAN- DO YOU LIKE PRESENTS? WOULD YOU LIKE ME TO COME ROUND ON XMAS EVE AND GIVE YOU ONE?
FNARR! FNARR!

AND... ER... IT'S NOT LONG NOW, YOU KNOW.
YIK! YIK!
?!
HOO! HOO!

5 MINUTES LATER...
COME ALONG NOW FINBARR - YOUR INNUENDO-BASED APPROACH HAS ALREADY CREATED QUITE ENOUGH TURMOIL FOR ONE DAY.
POLICE
ICE
POL
BEATING UP YOUNG KIDS EH? JUST WAIT TIL WE GET YOU DOWN THE NICK, SUNSHINE.

AT HOME THAT NIGHT...
MRS. SAUNDERS - I WONDER IF YOU MIGHT CARE TO PUT ME UP THIS EVENING.

YOU KNOW I'M ALWAYS HAPPY TO ACCOMMODATE YOU, MR. GIMLET.
K-YUK! K-YUK!

YOU'RE WELCOME TO POP IN MY PLACE ANY TIME.
!!

I'VE BROUGHT SOME DECORATIONS. I THOUGHT YOU'D LIKE ME TO DROP THEM FOR YOU.
HAAR! HAAR!

THERE'S THIS TREE TOO - FINBARR. AS I ALWAYS SAY - IF YOU'RE GOING TO HAVE ONE, MAKE SURE IT'S A BIG ONE!
HOOOF! HOOOF!

IT WON'T GO THROUGH THAT DOOR THOUGH. YOU'RE GOING TO HAVE TO TAKE IT UP THE BACK PASSAGE.
ARF! ARF!
SNURK! SNURK!

SO...
WATCH MY PAINTWORK! CAN YOU GET YOUR END AWAY?
EH? EH?
EH?
IT'S ALLRIGHT, MRS. SAUNDERS. DON'T BE AFRAID TO GIVE IT A GOOD PULL...
EH? EH?

I'VE GOT A GOOD SIX INCHES MY END.

HUAAARR! HUAAARR!
GAK! GAK! GAK! GAK!
KER-SNIP! KER-SNIP!
YUBB! YUBB!
FNURR! FNURR!
HO! HO!

SHORTLY...
WHAT ABOUT THE BUNTING?
I'D LIKE TO GET IT UP TONIGHT IF AT ALL POSSIBLE.

BUT I HAVE NO FESTIVE PAPER!
DON'T WORRY. I'VE GOT A PART-TIME JOB AT THE CREPE PAPER FACTORY. I'VE HAD A FEW ROLLS ON THE BACK SEAT OF MY CAR JUST LATELY...
FYAF! FYAF!

I'LL SLIP YOU A LENGTH IF YOU LIKE.
WOOF! WOOF!
HO! HO!
PHWOOAARR!!!

OOH! THERE'S ALL PINE NEEDLES IN ME PILE!
I HOPE IT WON'T SPOIL - I LIKE A NICE SHAG ON THE CARPET.
WUUOOAAR! WUUOOAAR!

ANYWAY - I RECKON IT'S AN EARLY NIGHT FOR ME AND YOUR MOTHER FINBARR. WE'RE DELIVERING PRESENTS IN LANCASHIRE AND NORTH WALES TOMORROW.
I'VE GOT TO GET MRS. SAUNDERS TO OLDHAM - THEN I'M GOING TO BANGOR AS FAST AS I CAN.

GOOUAH! GOOUAH!
EH?
EH?
ARF! ARF! ARF! ARF! ARF! ARF!
LATER...
I'LL TAKE THEM OFF - THEN YOU CAN STICK IT UP, MR. GIMLET.
LOOK AT THAT MRS. SAUNDERS - WELL HUNG OR WHAT?
HO! HO! SOUNDS LIKE MUM AND MR. GIMLET ARE PUTTING OUT THEIR CHRISTMAS STOCKINGS TOO!

*The evil pastimes of Britain's top telly stars*

# SEX AND MURDER!

**EXCLUSIVE**

By BOB SHITE

Past and present members of the popular EastEnders cast

**Soap stars from the cast of TV's EastEnders are heavily involved in satanism and Devil worship. That is the bombshell dropped today by a man who claims to have witnessed top soap stars taking part in an evil black magic ceremony culminating in the MURDER of an innocent young girl.**

Adult bookshop owner Bill Henshaw claims that he hid only yards away and watched in horror as a top TV actress was forced to have sex with male collegues in a bizarre moonlit occult ritual. And he was **SICKENED** as another leading member of the EastEnders cast plunged a dagger through the heart of a naked virgin, before smearing himself in her blood.

An artist's impression of the scene as EastEnders stars 'danced naked in a moonlit ceremony'

## BONFIRE

"I was on my way home from the pub, when I got lost", Bill told us, his face pale as he recalled the terrifying events of that night. "It was dark, and my car had broken down, so I was making my way across some fields to look for a telephone. Suddenly I noticed a light in woods nearby. It was a bonfire of some sort.

## NAKED

When I got closer I noticed people dancing around the fire. They were all naked. At first I thought they must have escaped from the local loony bin, but then I recognised one of their faces. It was Dennis Watts, the landlord of the Queen Vic pub in EastEnders. He was surrounded by other members of the cast. I was completely amazed by it all, so I hid in some bushes to find out what was going on.

## NAKED

They were all dancing frantically, and in the soft, flickering yellow light of the fire I could see beads of sweat rolling around the contours of their naked bodies", said Bill. "All the time they were chanting, the same words over and over again. It must have been Latin or something, as it made no sense to me. Then suddenly the bonfire seemed to flare up, and a huge cloud of orange smoke appeared. As it slowly began to clear, I could make out the shape of a gruesome figure which seemed to be hovering above the flames. It had horns, and goat's legs. I'd never seen anything like it before in my life".

## DEVIL

Experts who we spoke to suggested that this could have been the Devil himself, summoned up by the soap stars in order to receive their macabre sacrifice.

Bill continued. "Suddenly another member of the cast appeared. It was difficult to recognise him as he was wearing some sort of fancy, ceremonial robe, and his face was covered by a hideous mask. I'm not sure, but I think it could have been Arthur, the down trodden head of the Fowler household.

## NAKED

Then a young girl was led out of the shadows. She was naked. Suddenly I realised what was about to happen. I wanted to do something to stop them but I couldn't. If anyone had seen me I'd have been a gonner.

## BREAST

The man in the robes then produced a long silver dagger in the shape of an inverted cross, and plunged into the naked girl's breast. I simply couldn't watch. But I did. It was horrific".

## CHICKENS

After the killing the actors and actresses took turns to smear the girl's blood on their naked bodies, which were clearly visible in the glowing yellow light of the fire. "Then they all began to dance. It was as if they'd been hypnotised. People were being forced to have sex all over the place. It just became one great big orgy. I could hardly believe my eyes. I just sat and watched for about half and hour, thinking it must be a dream. But every time I pinched myself, I was still awake".

## ASHES

The next morning Bill retraced his steps and returned to the spot where the killing had taken place, only to find that all trace of the sick soap star's ceremony had been removed. "They had made a really good job. Even the ashes from the fire had gone. It was as if the whole thing had never happened".

Bill decided against reporting the incident to the police, "I had no proof. It was just my word against theirs. And who are the police going to believe? Me, or the entire cast of a well known TV soap opera".

A spokesman for the BBC denied that any member of the EastEnders cast was in any way connected with the occult, and suggested that Mr Henshaw's claims were totally ficticious. "This sounds like a load of rubbish to me", we were told. But Mr Henshaw remained adamant.

"They would deny it, wouldn't they", he said. "The chances are that they're all involved".

Mr Henshaw yesterday

In the past similar accusations made against BBC staff have also met with denials. As in 1983, when firemen were rumoured to have been called to the home of Sue Lawley to extinguish a "large whicker man" containing several chickens, which had been set alight in the back garden.

However, no comment has yet been made on the suggestion that TV football analyst Jimmy Hill is the head of an evil witches coven.

MORRIS DAY
SEXUAL PERVERT

LIKE ANY NORMAL PERSON, I LOVE TO SEE A GREAT BIG PAIR OF TITS FIRST THING IN THE MORNING, SO I ALWAYS BUY 'THE SUN'
Sun
TODAY! YOUNG GIRL EXPOSES HER BREASTS!

WOOAR! I'M BURSTING FOR A LOOK AT SOME BOOBS! GIVE ME A COPY OF THE SUN WILL YOU
I'M SORRY SIR, WE'VE SOLD OUT

NEVER MIND. THE STAR WILL DO. OR FAILING THAT, THE SPORT.
WE'VE GOT NO STARS EITHER
... BUT I HAVE SEVERAL COPIES OF THE SPORT. THAT'LL BE 25 PENCE.

BAH! CALL THOSE TITS? THIS PAPER IS SO BADLY PRINTED YOU CAN BARELY MAKE THEM OUT!
LOOK AT THE JUGS ON HER!
Mirror
HOW ABOUT THE MIRROR?

THE DAILY MIRROR?! THAT'S A RUBBISH PAPER! THEY COVER UP ALL THE NIPPLES IN THAT

AH! THAT GENTLEMAN OVER THERE HAS A COPY OF THE SUN. HE'LL NOT MIND IF I HAVE A SWIFT LOOK AT THE TITS

EXCUSE ME, BUT CAN I HAVE A QUICK GLANCE AT PAGE THREE?
PARDON?
Sun
BANG
BIG DISASTER KILLS PEOPLE
I'LL NOT BE A SECOND. I JUST WANT TO GET A QUICK EYEFULL

HERE. YOU CAN TAKE THAT PAGE. I'VE READ IT.
RIP!!
THANK YOU VERY MUCH!

BAH!!
RHUBARB RHUBARB

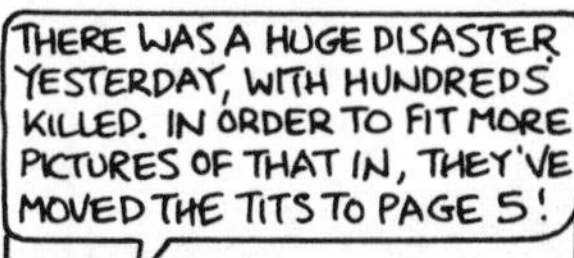
THERE WAS A HUGE DISASTER YESTERDAY, WITH HUNDREDS KILLED. IN ORDER TO FIT MORE PICTURES OF THAT IN, THEY'VE MOVED THE TITS TO PAGE 5!

DEATH DISASTER PICTURE SPECIAL
SORRY! TODAYS TITS ON PAGE 5

BLOODY HELL! IF I DON'T GET SOME BAZOOKAS INTO FOCUS PRETTY SOON I'M GONNA BLOW A FUSE!
LUCKILY I KEEP AN EMERGENCY SUPPLY OF GLOSSY MALE INTEREST MAGS IN MY WARDROBE

OH NO! MY WIFE'S BEEN SPRING CLEANING. SHE MUST HAVE THROWN THEM ALL OUT!

MR. DAY, THIS PARCEL ARRIVED FOR YOU WHILE YOU WERE OUT
OH... ERM... RIGHT! IT'S PROBABLY NOTHING. JUST LEAVE IT WITH ME, MRS. MOP.

THIS MUST BE MY SUNDAY TIMES COLOUR MAGAZINE BOOK CLUB MEMBERSHIP AT LAST!!

I ORDERED THE FULLY EXPLICIT 'SEX TODAY,' WITH OVER 250 FULL COLOUR PHOTOGRAPHS - THAT'S OVER 500 KNOCKERS!

NO... EVEN BETTER! IT'S THE 48 TRIPLE 'X' RATED ADULT ONLY PORN VIDEOS I SENT OFF FOR LAST MONTH
KNOCKERS
SAUCY BIG GIRLS
EXCELLENT! LOOKS LIKE I'M IN FOR A GOOD NIGHTS VIEWING!

OH SHIT! I HAVEN'T GOT A VIDEO

NEVER MIND. THERE'S ALWAYS GOOD OLD CHANNEL FOUR. YOU CAN USUALLY RELY ON THEM FOR A FOREIGN FILM WITH SUBTITLES AND TITS ALL OVER THE SHOP!
HERE GOES...

BLOODY HELL! OPERA! WHAT A WASTE OF TIME AND MONEY. IT'S DEAD BORING. YOU CAN'T UNDERSTAND A WORD THEY SAY, AND ALL THE BIRDS ARE FAT AND THEY NEVER GET THEIR TITS OUT!

AAAAOOOOOOOH!
OOOOOOOEE
OOOOOOOO-OH!

JUST WAIT TILL THIS SATELLITE TELLY GETS GOING! I'VE GOT MY DISH UP ALREADY... PHOARR!!
THEY GET IT IN ITALY. IT'S GREAT. TITS. BUMS. FANNY. THE LOT.

MMM... THAT REMINDS ME. IT'S FRIDAY. OUR NEXT DOOR NEIGHBOUR SOMETIMES HAS A BATH ON FRIDAY. AND SHE'S GOT REAL WHOPPERS!
THIS CALLS FOR BINOCULARS AND AN ALL-NIGHT STAKE-OUT!

SEVERAL HOURS LATER...
MORRIS, ARE YOU COMING TO BED?
NOT NOW. CAN'T YOU SEE I'M BUSY
CD. ST 89

Black BAG
THE FAITHFUL BORDER BIN LINER

Peeble's favourite binliner often used to act as a guide bag for little Timmy, a blind boy with an amazing sense of smell.

"Shh! Bag", said Timmy. "I can smell fertilizer bags behind the waterfall and they may be in trouble, let's go and investigate!"

Timmy was right.
The pair had stumbled across an illegal bag fighting ring: Ruffians who would kidnap old bags and make them fight to the death.

"We must move quickly", said Timmy. "You divert the river into the cave and I'll sniff my way to the police station."

With one mighty shove the muscular binliner dislodged the rock and sent the water crashing into the cave.

As the cave started to fill up with water the ruffians tried to escape, but it was no use.

The ruffians all perished in the flooded cave, but Black Bag managed to rescue the sodden bags, and that was the main thing.

"Thank you for saving my two best bags," said the farmer. "They look a wee bit waterlogged but I know how to fix them."

After Bag left, the farmer was as good as his word and gave them both a special treat - a hundred weight of warm horse manure each.

# SOUP IS SEXY!

## So says Doctor in fascinating book about soup

Soup guzzling Goss brothers (left) and 'horny' Jonathon Ross

**Soup is sexy. That's the saucy claim being made in a new book published this month. For author Dr. Karl Lipton believes that soup drinking can lead to improved sexual performance. In his book, 'All About Soup', he reveals that saucy dishes like minestrone and mushroom can act as an aphrodisiac.**

"Certain soups are sexier than others", explains Karl, a former lecturer in soup at Warwick University. He named French onion and oyster soup as two of the sexiest starters, and claimed that other soups — like turnip — are a turn off.

### OXTAIL

We decided to find out what kind of soup the stars prefered.

Every night, chat show host **JONATHAN ROSS** tucks into a steaming bowl of oxtail. "Jonathan comes home from work tired and exhausted", his wife Jane told us. "But one bowl of his favourite beefy brown broth is all it takes to put the lead back in his pencil", said Jane.

"It makes me a horny devil", Jonathan told us yesterday.

### SHARK

A Buckingham Palace insider revealed that at 40, **PRINCE CHARLES** is steering clear of sexy soups, plumping instead for brown Windsor. "As a result it's considered 'unlikely' that there'll be any further additions to his family", our source commented.

Off stage sexy Bros twins **MATT** and **LUKE GOSS** polish off gallons of shark's fin soup, and on stage the fans go wild. Meanwhile Ken, the third member of the band, sips away at a lukewarm bowl of lentil.

## French onion and oyster are among the sexiest

This amazing link between soup and sex is not a recent discovery, as Dr. Lipton explains in his book. 'In Papua New Guinea, natives serve up bowls of boring cauliflower soup as a primitive form of birth control. It's a tradition that goes back many centuries'.

### BORING

Dr. Lipton's book also provides a fascinating insight into the history of our favourite soups. For example, it explains how soup was often considered boring until the day in 1872 when French chef Jean Louis Crouton accidentally spilt a bowl of fried bread into a pot of soup he was busy preparing at his restaurant in Paris. "The resulting dish went down a storm with guests", Dr. Lipton told us. "And his subsequent invention, the crouton, is now served with soups in restaurants throughout the world". Although the restaurant no longer stands, the street in Paris where the discovery occured has since been renamed 'Rue de Crouton'.

## MANY UNUSUAL SOUPS ARE RARELY HEARD OF

**We've all heard of everyday soups like tomato, cream of mushroom and vegetable. But in his book Dr. Lipton also casts light on a whole variety of unusual soups which are consumed around the world.**

**One of the strangest must surely be African tree soup, eaten by the nomadic Okwe-kwe tribe on the fringes of the Seranghetti desert. However Dr. Lipton fears that due to massive deforestation programmes currently underway in that region this once proud tribe and their unusual soup may soon disappear forever.**

### ESKIMOS

**Thousands of miles away in the freezing arctic wastelands, Eskimos look to the sea for their soups. One favourite is whale soup, which Dr. Lipton claims has the highest calorific value of any soup known to man. 'Eskimos have been known to survive for up to 8 weeks on one bowl of this soup alone', he says in his book.**

### SCIENTISTS

**Over the years many soups have disappeared from menus altogether. Dinosaur soup, once popular among cavemen, has not been served for over a million years. However the same is not true of mammoth soup. In 1922 Russian scientists working in a remote corner of Siberia discovered a mammoth preserved in the ice. This historic discovery not only provided palaeontologists with a remarkable opportunity to study the extinct species, but it also gave Russian chef's a chance to re-discover this popular prehistoric soup.**

## Doctor has tasted more than 5,000 varieties

**Dr. Lipton estimates that over the years he has tasted more than 5,000 different types of soup. However, there is one soup which he will never savour, as cooking it is strictly illegal. Dr. Lipton explains: "Many years ago bat's arse soup was a popular dish in the British Isles. However, it takes up to 200 bats to make a single bowl of the soup, and as they are now a protected species, it is simply no longer possible to make the soup".**

*Dr. Lipton's Book, 'All About Soup' is published by Omlette Books, priced £19.95.*

## After 25 years the question WHO KILLED KENNEDY? remain

# DID ELVIS KILL

## Startling new evidence links 'King of Rock'n'Roll' to Kennedy assasination

**It is now almost quarter of a century to the day since the assasination of President John F. Kennedy shook the world. Yet despite the passing of time, an air of mystery still surrounds the President's death. Twenty-five years on the question is still being asked — Who DID kill the President?**

Officially the case closed many years ago. According to the history books Lee Harvey Oswald pulled the trigger on that fateful day in Dallas in 1963. But Oswald's guilt was never proven, and subsequently rumours of mafia involvement and Government cover ups have abounded.

### INCREDIBLE

But now new evidence has come to light — incredible evidence linking Elvis Presley, the late 'King of Rock 'n' Roll', to the killing. Evidence which, in weeks to come, could have startling repercussions both inside The Whitehouse and across the entire pop music industry of the world.

### UNLIKELY

For the last 15 years Archibald Gubbins has dedicated his life to uncovering the truth surrounding Kennedy's death. And he is now convinced that the man who shot the President was in fact Elvis Presley himself. Unlikely as it seems, Archie Gubbins now believes he has all the necessary evidence to support his claims.

### CARAVAN

Archie first developed an interest in the case after a friend he'd met on holiday hinted at a possible Elvis link to the Kennedy killing. "My wife and I went to Rhyll for a week in 1973 and it turned out that the man in the caravan next to ours, who was called Derek, had been a secret agent with the FBI during the sixties. He didn't talk much about his work, but one night in the pub after he'd had a few drinks this tongue began to loosen. He mentioned how, shortly after Kennedy was shot, they had found a guitar string on the floor in the book depository overlooking the scene.

"Later, they discovered several rhinestones on and around the grassy knoll which Kennedy's car was passing when the shots rang out. These were identical to rhinestones worn by Presley on his stage clothing".

### COVER-UP

Archie was surprised to find no reference to this evidence in any of the official reports. "There had obviously been some sort of cover-up, so I immediately became suspicious", he told us. My wife and I had also been Elvis fans for many years, and had often helped organise Elvis nights at our local pub. I felt that no matter what it took, I had to get to the bottom of the mystery".

### CLUES

In his search for the truth, Archie spent months carrying out painstaking research in his local library, scouring literally dozens of books in both the History and Popular Music sections for clues. He also spent hours watching videos of TV documentaries on the subject. But after years of research Archie had drawn a blank. Then one day, out of the blue, he got a lucky break.

**EXCLUSIVE**

"I was sitting in the kitchen browsing through a book on the subject when something caught my eye. It was a photograph taken at the scene of the assasination seconds before Kennedy was shot. In the background was the book depository building, and in a window I saw what appeared to be a human figure. But it was only a blur and I couldn't be sure.

"As luck would have it my brother-in-law, who is a former chemist and keen amateur photographer, was staying with me at the time. I showed the photograph to him and he said it might be possible to magnify it many times using a previously unknown photographic technique. He did this the next day and when I saw the results I couldn't believe my eyes. There, standing in the window was Elvis, as clear as day. I was absolutely speechless for several minutes".

**Elvis Aaron Presley — did the 'King' turn killer?**

Fifteen years after the fatal shot had been fired, Archie was now convinced that a cover-up had taken place. He immediately wrote and asked for Kennedy's remains to be exhumed so that an independent autopsy could be carried

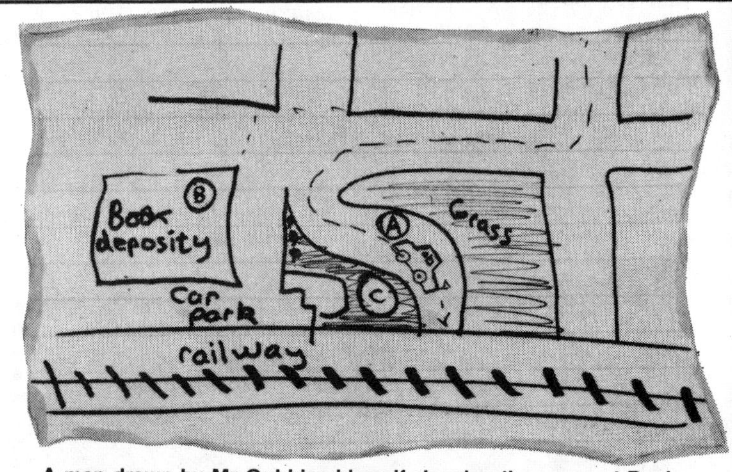


**A map drawn by Mr Gubbins himself showing the scene at Dealey Plaza, Dallas, at 12.30 pm, Friday 22nd November 1963. (A) The route taken by the Presidential limousine prior to the shots being fired. (B) The fifth floor window of the Dallas School Book Depository from which Mr Gubbins believes that Elvis fired three times. And (C) the 'Grassy Knoll' where rhinestones were found similar to those often worn by the singer. "In the car park to the rear of the grassy knoll several witnesses claim to have seen a man who looked a bit like Colonel Tom Parker, Elvis's manager", says Mr Gubbins. "But they're all dead now", he added.**

**...nanswered. But now, the experts are asking a NEW question.**

# ...HE PRESIDENT?

This photographic enlargement shows Elvis clearly visible in the fifth floor window of the Book Depository seconds before the shots rang out.

out. "A friend of mine had worked in an abattoir and offered to do a pathologist's report for me", says Archie. However, his request was turned down.

### TRIGGER

"I decided to go ahead and do our own autopsy, using photographs of the President from a book in the library". The report confirmed what Archie already knew. "There was no doubt in my mind Elvis pulled the trigger".

### BARREL

But what motive would drive the King of Rock 'n' Roll to kill the President? What was going through the singer's mind when he took aim on that cold, grey, November lunchtime?

### BEATLES

One theory which Archie puts forward is that Kennedy, disillusioned with politics, was about to launch his own pop career. Already under threat from The Beatles, 'The King' feared that Kennedy may succeed in capturing his crown. However there is little hard evidence to support this notion.

### MONKEES

Archie believes that jealously was the real reason. "Apparently, Elvis had heard from a friend that Kennedy fancied his wife Priscilla and wanted to go out with her", Archie told us. "That's probably why he did it".

> **'I could confirm that the gunshot wound which killed President Kennedy would be consistent with him having been shot in the head by the type of bullet fired from a gun by Elvis Presley.'**
>
> KEVIN DOBSON
> FREELANCE PATHOLOGIST

According to Archie, further evidence was left by Presley in the words of songs which he recorded after the shooting. "One evening my wife and I began to notice strange, almost cryptic references to the murder in the words of Elvis's songs. It was almost as if he was leaving deliberate clues for us to find. I suppose it was his way of admitting his guilt.

### DESPAIR

"For example 'You saw me crying in the chapel' is, I believe, Elvis's way of asking God to forgive him. And in 'There goes my everything' he sums up his feelings of despair once it had dawned on him what a terrible thing he'd done.

### REMORSE

"But the words of 'Rock-a-Hula Baby' speak for themselves. Elvis was obviously overcome with remorse. I think killing President Kennedy was a mistake which Elvis regreted for the rest of his life".

Even sceptics would have to agree that the Kennedy assassination certainly did mark a turning point in Presley's career. From that point onwards he began to concentrate on slow, mournful ballads, he stopped touring and began to shy away from the public eye. He became a recluse inside his palatial Memphis home and subsequently lost control over his bowel movements.

## *'I know too much'*
## *-Archie fears for his life*

Despite all the evidence put forward by Mr Gubbins, the authorities steadfastly refuse to re-open the case. And Archie now fears that his knowledge of the true events of that grey November day in 1963 could put his own life at risk. "I'm convinced that the telephone box in our street is being bugged, and my car has been tampered with. It keeps slipping out of first gear, and I've had to have the clutch looked at twice in as many weeks. It's scary when you think about it. The kind of people I'm dealing with here are above the law".

### COINCIDENCE

"I know too much — just like Buddy Holly, Bill Haley and now The Big 'O'. It's more than just a coincidence that all three of them have died since Kennedy was killed".

### SINISTER

We rang the FBI to ask whether or not they were involved in a sinister cover-up of Elvis's part in the Kennedy killing, but it was only 5 am in America and there was nobody in.

● *OPINION page 36*

This remarkable photograph was taken by an eye witness on a polaroid camera and shows the trees to the rear of the grassy knoll. Using another photographic technique, a portion of the picture can be enhanced to show quite clearly the figure of a man, not unlike Colonel Tom Parker, standing amongst the trees

# ROGER MELLIE

# THE MAN ON THE TELLY

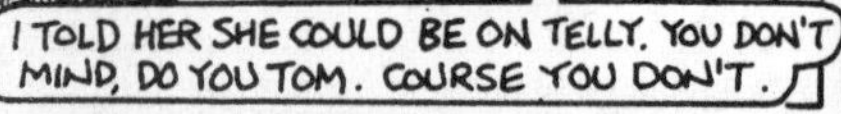

# QUEEN'S LETTERS LEAKED

## -Scotland Yard probe latest theft

**LETTERS addressed to the Queen have been sent to us by an anonymous source. And one of them, addressed to "The Occupier, Buckingham Palace", revealed that the Queen could have won up to £30,000 in a special prize draw.**

"Your name has been entered in our special prize draw", the letter explained. "To qualify simply complete and return the attached coupon". The neatly typed letter went on, "You will then be sent, entirely free of obligation, a copy of our latest catalogue".

### GAS

Another letter, also typed and posted somewhere in the London area, explained that according to an estimated meter reading in February of this year, the amount owing for gas consumption at the palace was £190.64. "If you consider this estimate to be unreasonable, please complete the dials shown on the reverse of this form and return the account immediately", it read.

### ELECTRIC

Another letter, contained in a white window envelope, listed a number of books which were available free of charge should the Queen wish to join a leading book club. Among the many titles available were The Collins World Atlas, A Road Map of Great Britain, a D.I.Y. Guide To Home Maintenance and The Illustrated Guide To Love Making (containing over 350 full colour photographs).

### RATES

We respect the privacy of the Royal Family and as a matter of journalistic principle refuse to publish these letters. All have now been handed to the police and a full scale investigation has been launched to identify their source. Officers from New Scotland Yard are believed to be working on the theory that a former Palace employee or postal worker could be responsible for the leak. When we tried to contact the Queen for her reaction we were told that her number was ex-directory.

# It's Biscuit Mania! - and that's official

**Britain has gone biscuit barmy! That's the news from biscuit manufacturers who have seen sales soar by an amazing 3% in the space of two years.**

Shop keeper Brian Wilson who has been selling biscuits for over twenty-five years, has never seen anything like it.

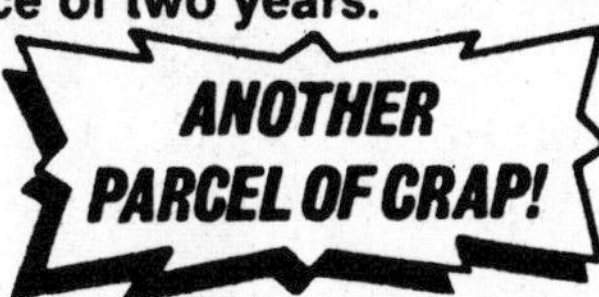


### BOURBON

"Customers have gone Custard Cream crazy", he told us from his corner shop in Preston, Lancs. "They're Bourbon bonkers — buying biscuits by the lorry load". Brian reckons that in the last week alone he's sold over 27 packets of biscuits — with a retail value of some £10.80.

And Lancashire isn't the only place that's gone Abbey Crunch crackers! Shoppers all over Britain are stuffing their supermarket trolleys with Hob Nobs, Digestives, Butter Puffs and Garibaldies galore. "One of our biggest sellers is the Tea Time Assortment tin", supermarket manager Ian McNicholl of Luton told us.

"It's incredible!" check out girl Terri Long confimed. "I've sold so many packets of biscuits this month I think I'm going Ginger Nuts!"

### ABBEY CRUNCH

A Government spokesman told us that sound economic policy was responsible for the recent rise in biscuit sales. "The Government are getting it right", he told us. "And as a result of increased prosperity more and more people are buying biscuits", he claimed.

### FIG NEWTON

And a spokesman for the National Biscuit Board of Control, the biscuit industry's self regulatory governing body, agreed. He is looking forward to a continuing increase in sales.

"People in Britain are already spending more on biscuits per head of population than they do on soap, fish or any other compatible product. And by the year 2000 we confidently expect this figure to have doubled".

### COCONUT RINGS

We rang roly-poly 'Hi-Di-Hi' funny man Ted Bovis, alias actor Paul Shane, to ask what his favourite biscuits were. But he wasn't in.

*It's the BIG question!*

# Has Fergie got a FAT ARSE?

**Ever since her marriage to Prince Andrew a cloud of controversy has surrounded the Duchess of York's bottom. In factories, shops, pubs and clubs all over Britain the question is being asked. "Has Fergie got a fat arse or what?"**

## YOU DECIDE

Well now's **YOUR** chance to join in with the debate of the decade, as we invite you to vote in our special postal ballot. All you have to do to register your opinion is fill in the coupon below:

● *OPINION* page 36

To: The Queen, Buckingham Palace, London

Dear Your Majesty

I do / do not* think that Fergie has got a fat arse.

Signed .................

*DELETE AS APPLICABLE

# I LIED FOR LOVE

CD Photography by Colin Davison

ADVERTISMENT

Nobody was more delighted than us by the marriage of Prince Andrew to Sarah Ferguson. And we joined with millions of others in congratulating the Royal couple on the birth of their daughter. Like all members of the Royal Family, we treat the Duke and Duchess of York with the respect and the dignity which they deserve.

*But a fat arse is a fat arse, no matter who it belongs to.*

**And in a free society it is our God-given right to say so.**

Elvis Presley was close to us all. More than just a star, he was a friend to many. He was, and still is, a very special part of our lives.

*But nobody is above the law. If Elvis killed President Kennedy then we, the public, have a right to know.*

**And so have the parents of Lee Harvey Oswald.**

'Thou shalt not kill', the Bible tells us. And so do the do-gooders who argue against the return of capital punishment.

*But try telling that to the armed gangs who terrorise our banks and post offices. Or the unarmed bobby, lying dead in the street. They won't hear you.*

**These men of violence are animals. We should round them up like cattle, and shoot them like pigs.**

*(And it's about time we tooled the coppers up as well).*

# GOOD NEWS FOR FAT GULLIBLE BASTARDS!

## LOSE A STONE A DAY!

with SlimAlot

BEFORE

NO MORE FAT!

AFTER

As featured in this advert

HERE IS WHAT THE EXPERTS SAID:

"I would confirm that the most effective method of slimming is by the loss of excess body weight or 'fat'."
Professor Karl Budweiser
Associate Research Director
Institute of Remedial Health Therapy, Dresden

"I have carried out extensive scientific research into a completely different subject and this quote is used entirely out of context."
Dr. Boris Lubanski
Dept. of Nutrition
University of Illinois

"I sent £25 for the SLIMALOT diet over 2 months ago and have still heard nothing. I would not hesitate to recommend this diet to others."
Mrs P. Gitt
Manchester

**WARNING!**

SLIMALOT is so effective you may lose TOO MUCH weight. It may in fact be necessary for you to supplement your SLIMALOT diet by eating large quantities of all your favourite food. You should however consult your doctor if, after several years of over-eating, you suffer severe pain in your left shoulder and chest palputations.

**YOUR GUARANTEE**

If you can prove that you have not lost weight within 28 days, simply send us another £25. No quibbles.

"I can guarantee that my SLIMALOT diet will lose you weight. It can't fail. The fact that I am still a fat bastard myself is totally irrelevant."
Reg Jones
Managing Director
SLIMALOT (UK) LTD

**LOOK!** HOW MUCH WEIGHT DO YOU WANT TO LOSE? ☐ 1 stone ☐ 2 stone ☐ 3 stone ☐ 4 stone ☐ 5 or more

Tick any number of boxes you like.

Simply fill in the coupon and sent it, together with £25 to SLIMALOT (Dept V34), P.O. Box 123, London.

I am a fat gullible bastard and I enclose £25. I understand that I will never see this money again.

Signed ..........................

YOU ARE INVITED TO **DINE** WITH THE...

# BOTTOM INSPECTORS

LATE EVENING IN A WELL-TO-DO SUBURB AND NOTHING DISTURBS THE POLITE AFTER DINNER CONVERSATION BUT THE CLINK OF CRYSTAL GLASSES AND THE RUSSLE OF WAFER THIN MINT WRAPPERS...

OH JUCINDA THET WAS A *SERIOUSLY* SCRAMMY DINNER, WE SIMPLY *MAST* POOT THE DISHES IN THE MACHINE FOR YOU.
mmmh, lovely coffee, anyway as I was saying...
mmh, très delish!
DON'T BE SO SILLY VERITY-JANE, I'VE GOT TARQUIN QUITE WELL-TRAINED, HEVEN'T I DARLING?
YOU CHEEKY MITE YOU!

KNOCK! KNOCK! KNOCK!
I SEY OCTAVIA, DO YOU THINK THET COULD BE THEO END PIPPA ET THE DOOR?
I SHOULD DOIYT IT PIERS, YOU FORGETFUL SAUSAGE! LOOK IN YOUR FILO - THEY HEV AN OPERA BOOKING WITH CRAWFORD END DELPHINIA TONIGHT!

UNLESS YOU *SHOPPED YOUR FRIENDS*, EH?!
*WHAT?!* YOU MEAN YOU TRADED BOTTOM INFORMATION ABOUT *US* FOR YOUR FREEDOM?
*YES!* THET'S WHY HE MADE THET MYSTERIOUS PHONE CALL EARLIER!
MY GOD! A *FIFTH-BOTTOMIST!*

WAIT A MOMENT! *WHAT ARE YOU DOING?*
OH, JUST A MEASUREMENT.
*BAT WHAT ABOIYT AAH ARRANGEMENT?*

HA! YOU DON'T REALLY THINK YOU CAN PLEA-BARGAIN WITH THE OFFICE OF BOTTOM INSPECTION? HA! HA! 20-25 YEARS FOR YOU!
WHAT?
THESE ARE *THIRD DEGREE SKIDS*. ANOTHER CENTIMETRE AND THEY'D BE FOURTH DEGREE - PUNISHABLE BY *DEATH!* ... RIGHT! LOAD THEM *ALL* IN THE *BOTT-MARIA!*

*NEXT EPISODE* - **ESCAPE FROM Coldbotz!!**

TWO YEARS HAVE PASSED SINCE THE TRAGIC DEATH OF FISH-LIKE KEEPER BILLY THOMSON, AND FULCHESTER NOW FIND THEMSELVES FLOUNDERING AT THE FOOT OF THE FOURTH DIVISION. THE ONCE CROWDED TERRACES, ONCE ECHOING TO THE SOUNDS OF SUCCESS, ARE NOW BLEAK AND DESERTED....

TO BE CONTINUED...

## The page that's not afraid to kick you in the bollocks and then run away

# I like apple crumble

**STAR LETTER**

I like apple crumble. Have any other readers got favourite desserts?

Edgar Foulkes
Gloucester

***Come on, readers, what's your favourite pudding? Maybe it's rhubarb and custard or a Chelsea bun. Or maybe it's some other pudding. Write and tell us and we'll give a ten pound prize for the best favourite pudding we receive. Mark your envelope 'Top of the puds'.***

Are the British public cowards or just plain lazy? The other day, an old lady was attacked in broad daylight in our high street. I stood and watched for a good five minutes during which time not one person lifted a finger to help. Whatever happened to the Dunkirk spirit?

L. Norder
Camberly

I told my husband that I'd like a cheese plant for my birthday. Imagine my surprise when, on my last birthday, he handed me the deeds to a large dairy produce factory in Wales.

Mrs Godfrey
Weston-super-Mare

"Look, daddy is on fire!" said my daughter recently after my husband had lit up his pipe. We all laughed — except my husband that is. He believes that my 29 year old daughter's juvenile behaviour is the cause for some concern.

Mrs. P. Ratnor
Billingham

My hubby never listens to a word I say. Hardly surprising, as he ran off with another woman some 25 years ago.

Mrs. Myte
London

I told my husband how much I'd like a rubber plant for the front room. I almost fell through the floor when he made me the managing director of a large tyre factory in Yorkshire.

Mrs Godfrey
Weston-super-Mare

Money talks, or so the saying goes. Surely with today's technology this could become a reality. Imagine the advantages for blind people if battery operated coins were designed to speak their value when taken out of your pocket.

T McDermott
Bury

# Saved by a cuppa

A cup of tea once saved my life! I nipped into the kitchen to make one last week when an unexploded world war two bomb suddenly blew up in my front room. Hooray for the British cuppa!

M Stiff
Wimbledon

***Do you have interesting stories involving a cup of tea? Come on, let's hear it for the British cuppa! Send your letters to our Letterbox address, and mark your envelopes 'Hooray for the British cuppa!"***

I asked my husband for a coconut plant for Christmas. I could hardly believe my eyes when he bought me a desiccated coconut treatment factory in the West Indies. Do I win £5?

Mrs Godfrey
Weston-super-Mare

# I'm sick of loudmouth celebrities

Rarely does a day go by without some comedian, pop star or other jumped-up celebrity lecturing us on the damage we are doing to the environment, the ozone layer, rain forests etc.

I could give one or two of these fellows a lecture too — on the damage taking drugs has done to their brains.

Major Percy Reid
Hexborough

Divorce seems common these days. But not in our family. There were twelve of us, all married (there were no "homosexuals" in those days), and all of us have now celebrated Silver Weddings. (Except for my brother George. He was run over by a taxi in 1958).

Mrs. E. Long
Oldham

# TOP TIPS

**Don't waste money buying expensive binoculars. Simply stand closer to the object you wish to view.**

**S Goldhanger
Fulchester**

**Next time you decorate, put wallpaper up with blu-tac. It's much easier, and expensive paper can easily be removed and taken with you when you move house.**

**E McAndrews
Didsbury**

**Cyclists. Next time you're out on your bike take a tin bath and about 4 or 5 gallons of water in plastic containers. In the event of a flat tyre this will help you locate any punctures you may have.**

**Andy Hodgson
Manchester**

**Increase the weight of your husband's trousers by attaching onions to the belt loops.**

**Uncle Len
Ruddington**

**An elastic band with a dab of toothpaste makes an economical substitute for chewing gum, and it's better for your teeth.**

**K Barker
Barrow-in-Furness**

**When buying a camera, always purchase a second one so that if you sell it, you can take a picture of it for advertising purposes.**

**A Harmer
Frodsham**

**Avoid waiting for a doctors appointment by making one for 9.00 a.m. every morning. If you wake up feeling well, simply phone up and cancel it.**

**R Dury
Ruddington**

**AVOID over-ordering milk by placing your fridge just outside your front gate. The milkman can then check your day to day requirement for himself.**

**Phillip Torr
Essex**

**IF you have an artificial leg, make it unoticeable by wearing long trousers.**

**O. Craig
Stonehaven**

**By making a simple periscope out of toilet roll tubes and small pocket mirrors, it is possible to watch T.V. from under your floorboards.**

**P N Thorne
Bristol**

**Thicken up runny low-fat yoghurt by stirring in a spoonful of lard. Simple.**

**P Raker
Chatham**

**Annoy your neighbour by sprinkling nettle and other weed seeds into his flower bed while he's out.**

**Stef Miller
Sheffield**

**Cut a chair in half, nail a plank between the two pieces and you have yourself an attractive garden bench.**

**A Harmer
Frodsham**

**Stop visitors using your phone without asking by taking it off the hook and sitting on the receiver.**

**Nick Dwyer
Brighton**

**Impress friends by making a list of all the objects in your front room and then invite them over to play I-spy. Watch their faces as you keep winning!**

**J Cowell
Milton Keynes**

# Are you a TRUE animal lover?

**We all love kittens, puppies and goldfish. In Britain today almost everyone has owned a pet at one stage or another. But are we really a nation of animal lovers? There's more to being a TRUE animal lover than simply taking your dog for a walk, feeding pigeons or throwing buns to an elephant.**

## Here's your chance to find out!

Here's a fun to answer questionnaire that will reveal whether **YOU** and your friends are real animal lovers or merely fair weather fans. Answer all the questions, a b or c, then tot up your final score.

1. A friend invites you out for dinner at a high class restaurant. Which of the following meals would you choose?

*a. A raw, bleeding, freshly killed steak.*
*b. A couple of small, well cooked sausages, with mash.*
*c. An organically grown lettuce.*

2. You are driving along a country lane late at night when you hit and kill a small, fluffy rabbit which had frozen in your headlights. What would you do?

*a. Stop the car and throw the rabbit in the boot. Your wife might be able to chuck it in a pie or some-thing.*
*b. Drive on as if nothing has happened.*
*c. Have the dead rabbit stuffed caringly by a qualified taxidermist and display it in a prime position in your home.*

3. You awake to find a spider in the bath. What would you do?

*a. Strike it repeatedly with the toilet brush, wipe up its remains on a piece of tissue paper then flush them down the toilet.*
*b. Go to a neighbour's house and ask whether, under the circumstances, it would be possible to use their bath instead.*
*c. Construct a small rope ladder using matchsticks and lengths of string, then hang it over the side of the bath enabling the spider to escape.*

4. The circus comes to town and your kids plead with you to take them. What would you do?

*a. Take them along, buy some pop corn, sit back and enjoy the show.*
*b. Take them, but encourage them to applaud only human acts, and not those which involve animals.*
*c. Help them to paint protest banners, take them along to the Big Top, then organise them into a peaceful picket line outside the entrance.*

5. While out shopping on your local High Street, you notice one shop is selling expensive fur coats. How would you react? Would you:

*a. Go in and buy the most expensive coat.*
*b. Ask to try a few coats on, but postpone any decision to buy until you have had time to think it over.*
*c. Put superglue into the shop's locks, and then return later that evening to fire bomb the premises.*

6. Whilst enjoying a seaside holiday you hire a two seater paddle boat on the beach. Suddenly, you notice a big Japanese factory whaling ship in hot pursuit of a large, helpless whale. What would you do?

*a. Take a photograph of the whale being killed and show it to friends on your return.*
*b. Ignore the commotion and continue with your leisurely paddle.*
*c. Paddle frantically in the direction of the ship and try to position yourself between the harpoonist and the whale.*

7. You are enjoying afternoon tea on the patio when a small fox suddenly leaps over the wall and hides under your table. A few moments later the local squire and several well-to-do friends arrive on horseback with a pack of baying hounds and ask whether you have seen the fox. What would you do?

*a. Lift the table cloth to reveal the terrified animal, then retire to a safe distance to watch the hounds tear it apart.*
*b. Say nothing. After all, fair's fair. They should find the fox for themselves.*
*c. Tell them that you saw the fox in a village several miles away and send them in completely the wrong direction.*

8. A new neighbour invites you to a dog fight in his back garden. How would you respond?

*a. Gratefully accept the invitation and go along gleefully, hoping to win a few bob.*
*b. Pop in for a few minutes, so as not to appear rude.*
*c. Photograph the event from a vantage point in your own garden and compile a telling dossier of evidence against your neighbour which you would then forward to the RSPCA.*

9. Another one of your neighbours is a battery farmer, and he's going away on holiday. He asks if you would clip his chickens' beaks for him each morning. What would you do?

*a. Jump at the chance. It's a great opportunity to steal some eggs.*
*b. Agree to do it, but only if the money's right.*
*c. Accept the job, then hire a big lorry and take the chickens to the seaside and set them free.*

10. You buy your son a small puppy, however after returning from a long day out you find that it has soiled the doormat. Would you:

*a. Rub its snout in its own mess, kick it out of the house then arrange with the vet to have the animal destroyed.*
*b. Scold it roundly, and threaten it with a rolled up newspaper.*
*c. Save the puppy's embarrassment by pretending not to notice, then clean up the mess later after the pup has gone to bed.*

11. You are playing baseball on the beach with your kids when you spot a baby seal basking on a nearby ice flow. What would you do?

*a. Club it to death with your bat and use its pelt to make an attractive pencil case or similar present for your kids.*
*b. Ignore it. It'll probably go away.*
*c. Spray its coat with a harmless indelible green ink thus rendering it worthless to fur traders, then throw it back into the sea.*

12. You are watching a TV farming documentary when you witness a scene in which a pig is about to be slaughtered. How would you react? Would you:

*a. Continue to watch in a frenzy of excitement, setting your video to record the scene*
*b. Flick around to see if anything better is on.*
*c. Write a strong letter of complaint to the Director General of the BBC, enclosing a home made explosive device.*

13. While walking in the countryside your pet dog attacks and injures several sheep. What would you do?

*a. Take a rock from a dry stone wall and attempt to destroy the injured animals. It's the humane thing to do.*
*b. Take your dog home, pretending that nothing has happened, and remember to bring a lead with you next time.*
*c. Scold your dog for misbehaving, then apologise to the farmer, offering to pay for repairs to the damaged sheep.*

14. You are at a protest about South African fruit. Suddenly a policeman on horseback starts hitting you about the head and shoulders with a long stick. How would you react? Would you:

*a. Scatter crudely welded spikes on the ground to injure the horse and dismount the rider.*
*b. Let off a starting pistol in the hope of unsettling the horse without causing any injury.*
*c. Give the horse a sugar lump, then demand that the policeman dismounts before striking him with your placard.*

15. Your daughter keeps a pet rabbit in a hutch in the back garden. One night you awake to find your next door neighbour, who works in a shampoo factory, has climbed into the garden and is putting something into the rabbit's eyes. What would you do?

*a. Ignore the incident and go back to bed.*
*b. Consider heightening your garden wall to prevent any similar intrusions in the future.*
*c. Organise a protest march to your next door neighbour's factory, and distribute leaflets to houses in your street suggesting that people boycott their particular brand of shampoo.*

## How did you do?

**Award yourself 3 points for every C you answered, 2 points for a B and 1 point for each A. Then tot up your score and see how you rate:**

### 40 or over

**Look out David Attenborough. You really are an animal's best friend. You treat them as your equal, refusing to ill treat them or stand by and watch them suffer. And you probably don't eat them very often either. You're a true animal lover, and in return the animals will love you too.**

### 20 to 39

**Not bad, but you can't call yourself a REAL animal lover. You obviously enjoy the company of certain animals, and would never be cruel to a pet. But try being more friendly to other, less attractive animals, like anteaters and slugs. They have feelings too, you know.**

### 19 or less

**You heartless bastard. What have animals ever done to you? People like you are worse than animals. How would you like to be slaughtered by a herd of cattle, then cooked in an oven? No. It isn't very nice when you think about it, is it? Well, one day you probably will be. So don't come running to us for help.**

# BAD NEWS FOR BALDIES

**We all know that bald men look stupid, with their shiny heads, their silly sticky-out ears and those ridiculous wiggly veins on their temples. But the next time you see a bald man, before you stop to point and laugh, think for a moment. One day YOU could be bald.**

Although it's something we prefer not to think about, sooner or later eight out of ten per cent of men in Britain will have suffered partial hair loss by the time they're forty. And a staggering 50% of adult males will be totally bald by the year 2000. Baldness due to loss of hair is, quite simply, becoming an epidemic.

### OZONES

The reasons for the dramatic increase in baldness are many fold. Additives in our food, the ozone layer and the latest appearance of Haley's comet are all contributory factors in making people go bald. But what can be done to save your hair once the early stages of baldness set in?

### ACID RAIN

Dr Ulf Jergensen is Hair Expert at Sweden's University of Upsala, and he has bad news for baldies. "Nothing whatsoever can be done to prevent the onset of baldness once hair loss has begun. All your hair will fall out onto the floor and all over your coat, and you will be bald for the rest of your life," says the doctor.

### CARBON MONOXIDE

But Dr Jergensen hastens to add that although the disease is incurable, unsightly baldness can effectively be concealed. "With today's technology bald people can almost look normal," says the doctor. He recommends four ways of disguising embarrassing loss of hair.

1. Wearing a large colourful hat which comes down to just below your ears.
2. Wearing a clump of pretend hair – a 'wig' – on the top of your head.
3. In cases where hair loss is not complete, any remaining hair can be sweapt across the bald bit, giving the impression of a completely full and healthy head of hair.
4. People with lots of money may prefer to have hair taken from their bottoms and planted in several small holes in their head which have been drilled in a realistic grid pattern.

## THE BALD TRUTH

*A lot of popular misconceptions exist surrounding the subject of baldness. Bald people are said to be more virile, more intelligent and able to swim faster than normal people. But they aren't.*

*Here are the true facts about bald people.*

- *Bald people are sterile.*
- *Girl's don't want to go out with bald people.*
- *Baldness is hereditary, but you can also get it from toilet seats.*
- *Bald people are often slow thinking, clumsy and 'drunk' in appearance because of their brains getting cold.*
- *Bald people tend to lead sad and shallow lives, often drifting towards alcoholism and homelessness, due to their loss of hair.*

Barry the Cat
The weird tale of a strange boy acrobat who's mission in life is to uphold the law of England and bring all wrongdoers to justice ...
One day, Barrington Granger, quiet, bespectacled Barnford schoolboy and his pal, Colin Burton visited Barnford Agricultural show.
GOSH, BARRINGTON, IT'S AWFULLY HOT.
YES, LET'S HAVE SOME ICE-CREAM, COLIN OLD CHAP.
But, as the two chums queued for their ices ...
I SAY, BARRINGTON, THEY LOOK IN A HURRY.
HMMMM!
THIS IS A STICK-UP!
In the excitement, no one noticed young Barrington slip away.
HAND OVER THE CASH AND YOU WON'T GET HURT!
But as the crooks jumped into their waiting getaway car ...
NOT SO FAST, YOU BAD MEN. YOU DIDN'T BARGAIN ON MEETING BARRY THE CAT.
At once, Barrington changed into the black leather suit of Barry the Cat — for he and the feline crime buster were one and the same person.
Meanwhile ...
HEY, TED, THERE MUST BE ALMOST TWENTY POUNDS HERE.
COME ON, LET'S GET OUT OF HERE!
I'LL TAKE THAT, HURR HURR!
With fearless cat-like agility, Barry leapt from the branches.
WHAT THE ...
OOOYAH!
LOOK. ISN'T THAT YOUNG BARRING-TON GRANGER?
YES. WHAT ON EARTH IS HE DOING DRESSED UP LIKE THAT?

As the car screeched away, Barry knew he must act fast.
OOH, MY SHOULDER. I THINK IT'S BROKEN.
Taking the rope from his cat-belt, he swung it around his head ...
THIS WILL PUT PAID TO THEIR PLANS.
... and hurled it towards the getaway car.
HA. GOING SOMEWHERE?
Barry's cat-like aim was true.
But as the claw hook found it's mark ...
WAAAAH!
GROAN!
Several minutes later ...
CRIPES! IT'S THAT KID AGAIN.
YES, HE'S ATTACHED HIMSELF TO THE BACK OF THE CAR.
THIS'LL GET RID OF HIM.
The driver turned the big car on a sixpence ...
OH! NO! A TREE!
OOOF!
COME ON LADS. LET'S TURN HIM OVER!
OOH! WHERE AM I?
The evil gang gave Barry a proper kicking.
ME NEXT!
OKAY, LADS. ENOUGH. LET'S GO!
OOF! AGH!
Later, in the first aid tent ...
YOU'VE BEHAVED VERY FOOLISHLY, YOUNG MAN.
TACKLING ARMED ROBBERS INDEED!
BARRINGTON, WHAT ON EARTH WERE YOU DOING AND WHY WERE YOU WEARING THAT RIDICULOUS OUTFIT?
COUGH. GASP!

ROGER MELLIE
THE MAN ON
THE TELLY
BOLLOCKS!

AH ROGER! WOULD YOU BE ABLE TO PRESENT 'CELEBRITY KEYHOLE' THIS WEEK? I'M AFRAID FLOYD GROSSMAN IS OFF SICK
YEAH. NO PROBLEM TOM
Variety

THAT'S GREAT. ERM... YOU HAVE SEEN THE SHOW BEFORE HAVEN'T YOU
OH YEAH. LOADS OF TIMES...
THAT'S THE ONE WHERE THE BIRD WITH A BIG ARSE FLIES AROUND IN A HELICOPTER, INNIT?
Variety

NO NO NO! IT'S THE SHOW WHERE WE GO AND FILM A MYSTERY CELEBRITY'S HOUSE, AND THE VIEWERS HAVE TO TRY AND GUESS WHO LIVES THERE
OH YEAH... RIGHT. I'M WITH YOU
Variety

WE'RE FILMING AT No. 123 FULCHESTER PARK MANSIONS TOMORROW. I'LL MEET YOU THERE AT TEN, AND FOR GOD'S SAKE DON'T BE LATE!
SURE THING TOM. I'LL CATCH YOU LATER

THE NEXT DAY...
WHERE THE HELL IS ROGER? I TOLD HIM TO BE HERE BY TEN
TOM! OVER HERE!

WHAT THE HELL ARE YOU DOING UP THERE ROGER?
THERE WAS NO ANSWER AT THE DOOR, SO I WENT ROUND THE BACK AND PUT A WINDOW THROUGH

COME DOWN AT ONCE! YOU'RE IN THE WRONG HOUSE! YOU SHOULD BE IN THAT ONE!
WELL... FUCK ME!
F.T.V.

NEXT DOOR IS IT? I DUNNO. THEY ALL LOOK THE BLEEDIN' SAME TO ME

EVENTUALLY, INSIDE THE RIGHT HOUSE...
OKAY. ARE WE ALL SET TO START?
TOM! LOOK AT THIS!

A FUCKIN' DRINKS CABINET! SMART, EH? WHAT'S EVERYONE HAVING?
PUT IT AWAY ROGER! WE'RE NOT SUPPOSED TO TOUCH ANYTHING

FOR GOODNESS SAKE, TRY TO REMEMBER YOU'RE IN SOMEONE ELSE'S HOUSE!
OH YEAH... WHO'S GAFF IS THIS ANYWAY?

THE HOUSE BELONGS TO POP STAR RICK SPANGLE, BUT THE VIEWERS AREN'T TO KNOW THAT...
YOU'LL POINT OUT A FEW CLUES AS WE GO ALONG. COME ON, LET'S GET STARTED!

AS YOU MOVE AROUND THE HOUSE, TRY TO DROP A FEW SUBTLE CLUES. YOU COULD POINT OUT THE LARGE RECORD COLLECTION FOR EXAMPLE
FTV
NO PROBLEM TOM. JUST LEAVE IT TO ME

ACTION!
WHOEVER LIVES HERE MUST BE FUCKIN' LOADED - LOOK AT ALL THESE POSH VASES N' STUFF...
I BET THEY'RE WORTH A BOMB!

AND LOOK AT ALL THESE RECORDS. HEY! I BET HE'S A POP STAR, LIKE THAT BLOKE... ER....
WHAT'S-IS-NAME... RICK SOMETHING OR OTHER...
HOLD IT!
THE DEAD GOODS

THAT'S NOT A CLUE, ROGER. YOU'VE PRACTICALLY GIVEN IT AWAY! AND PLEASE CAN YOU CUT OUT THE SWEARING!
COME ON. LET'S TAKE A LOOK AROUND UPSTAIRS

UPSTAIRS...
RIGHT. LET'S HAVE A LOOK IN HERE... OOOOH! IT'S THE BATHROOM
FTV

CAN WE HOLD IT THERE FOR A SECOND TOM. I'M GONNA HAVE A QUICK DUMP! I HAD A BIT OF A CURRY LAST NIGHT - A REAL RING STINGER!
CHRIST ALMIGHTY!
HURRY UP THEN

FIFTEEN MINUTES LATER...
JESUS! MY POOR ARSE!
EEH! NEVER AGAIN TOM, NEVER AGAIN!

CAN WE FILM IN THERE NOW ROGER?
OOH, I THINK I'D GIVE IT TEN MINUTES IF I WAS YOU TOM!

LATER
WELL, HERE WE ARE IN THE BEDROOM
SO LET'S LOOK AROUND FOR A FEW MORE CLUES

JUDGING BY THIS PAIR OF KNICKERS, AND THE STATE OF THE BEDSHEETS, I'D SAY WHOEVER LIVES HERE'S GOT A TART ON THE GO!

AND WHAT'S ALL THIS, HIDDEN ON TOP OF THE WARDROBE? THIS LOOKS INTERESTING...
TITS AND FANNYS
EEH! THE HORNY BASTARD!

I DON'T THINK I'VE SEEN THIS ONE BEFORE, ACTUALLY
CUT!
TITS AND FANNY
MIND YOU, THERE'S SOME GOOD STUFF IN HERE!

HEY TOM! WILL YOU LOOK AT THE SIZE OF THOSE!
ROGER. PLEASE REMEMBER THIS IS A FAMILY SHOW
I THINK PERHAPS WE SHOULD GO DOWNSTAIRS NOW!

DON'T BE DAFT TOM! THIS IS JUST STARTING TO GET INTERESTING
THIS STUFF MAKES GREAT T.V. TOM. THE PUNTERS LOVE IT!

HEY! GET THE CAMERAS ROLLING. I'M GONNA HAVE A DIG AROUND IN THE ATTIC AND SEE WHAT ELSE I CAN FIND!
OH COME ON ROGER! DON'T BE RIDICULOUS

IT'S A BIT DARK UP HERE, TOM
CRACK!
VHS

CRASH!!

THERE'S NOT REALLY THAT MUCH TO SEE UP THERE TOM. SHALL WE GO DOWNSTAIRS NOW EH?

COME ON ROGER. WE'LL FILM A QUICK PIECE IN THE KITCHEN, THEN THE SOONER WE GET OUT OF HERE THE BETTER
THE KITCHEN EH? GREAT! I'M FUCKIN' STARVING!

COME ON THEN. LET'S THINK OF SOME CLUES
WHY NOT LOOK IN THE FRIDGE AND FIND OUT WHETHER OR NOT THE OWNER IS A HEALTHY EATER

SO...
I THINK I'LL TAKE A LOOK IN THE FRIDGE TO SEE WHETHER OR NOT THE OWNER IS A HEALTHY EATER!

HEY! BACON. EGGS. SAUSAGES. THE WORKS! WHO FANCIES A FRY UP?

THERE'S NO TIME FOR THAT ROGER! COME ON! I DON'T WANT TO BE AROUND WHEN MR. SPANGLE GETS BACK
COME ON TOM. THIS WON'T TAKE A SECOND. LOOK... I'LL TURN IT UP HIGH

HOW DO YOU LIKE YOUR EGGS TOM? SUNNY SIDE UP EH?

WHOOPS!

AN HOUR LATER
...YOU WILL OF COURSE BE FULLY COMPENSATED MR SPANGLE
FIRE
YOU DON'T NEED ME FOR ANYTHING ELSE DO YOU TOM? ONLY I'VE GOT A BIRD LINED UP FOR TONIGHT AND I DON'T WANT TO KEEP HER WAITING...
C.D. G.P.D. '89

# HAPPY EVER AFTER

But just as Stacey was settling down to a lonely night at home, the doorbell rang...

Shortly...
HAVE A GOOD TIME STACEY!
I'LL MEET YOU BACK HERE AT TWELVE. BUT DON'T BE LATE. I'VE GOT ANOTHER JOB TO DO THEN
The concert was everything Stacey had dreamed it to be. Bobby Stardust sang all his hit records, and the time just seemed to go flying by.
I WANT YOU BABY! OOOH YEAH!
OH BOBBY... I LOVE YOU
OOOH YEAH!

As soon as the concert was over, Stacey headed for the stage door, hoping to get one final glimpse of her hero...
SORRY LOVE. YOU CAN'T GO IN THERE

HEY MAN! IT'S COOL. THE CHICK'S ALRIGHT
BOBBY STARDUST!
ANYTHING YOU SAY MR STARDUST

Stacey was dumbstruck...
HEY BABY! I HOPE YOU DUG MY GIG
I SAW YOU IN THE FRONT ROW AND I WAS HOPING TO HAVE A WORD WITH YOU, YEAH?

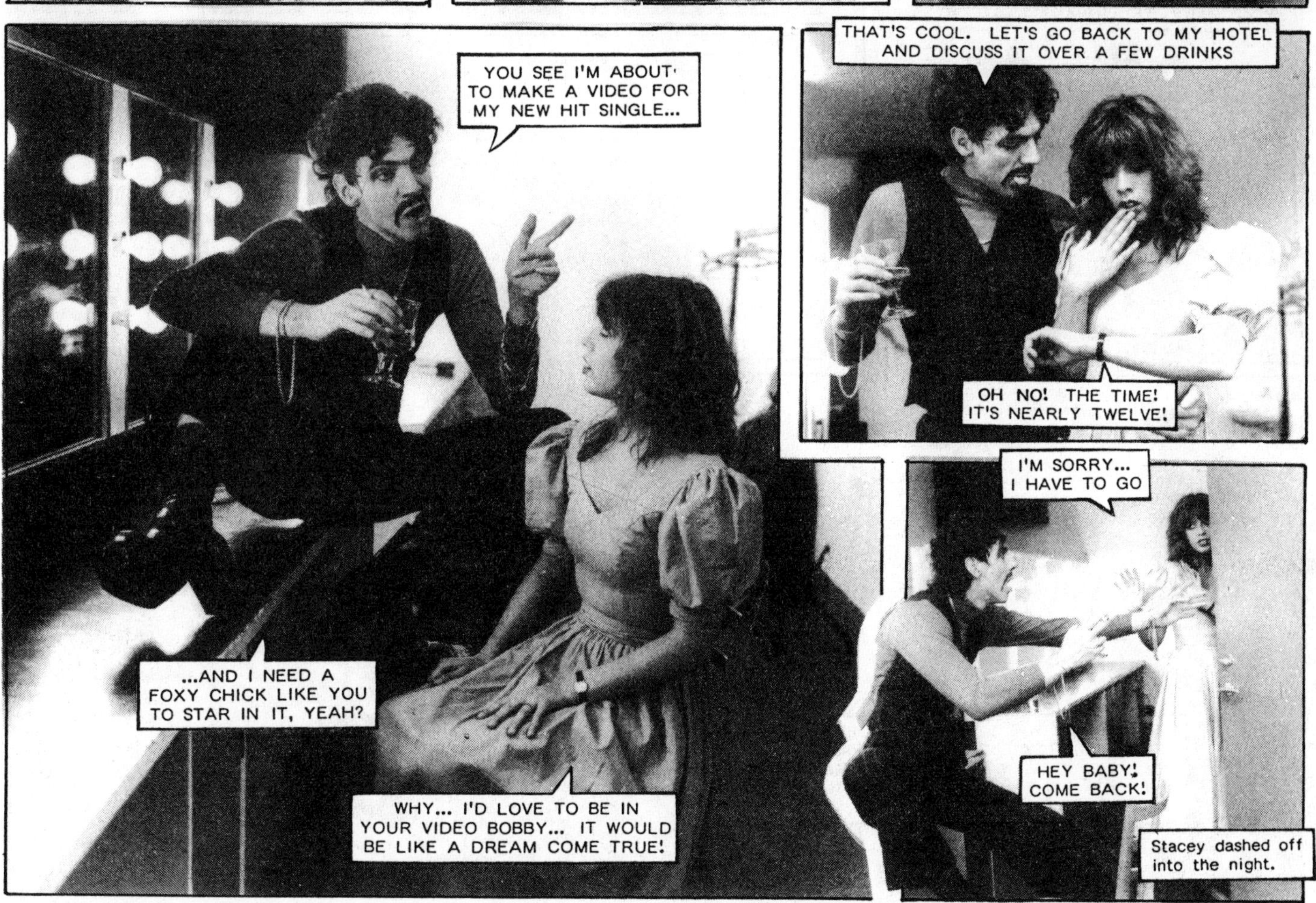
YOU SEE I'M ABOUT TO MAKE A VIDEO FOR MY NEW HIT SINGLE...
...AND I NEED A FOXY CHICK LIKE YOU TO STAR IN IT, YEAH?
WHY... I'D LOVE TO BE IN YOUR VIDEO BOBBY... IT WOULD BE LIKE A DREAM COME TRUE!
THAT'S COOL. LET'S GO BACK TO MY HOTEL AND DISCUSS IT OVER A FEW DRINKS
OH NO! THE TIME! IT'S NEARLY TWELVE!
I'M SORRY... I HAVE TO GO
HEY BABY! COME BACK!
Stacey dashed off into the night.

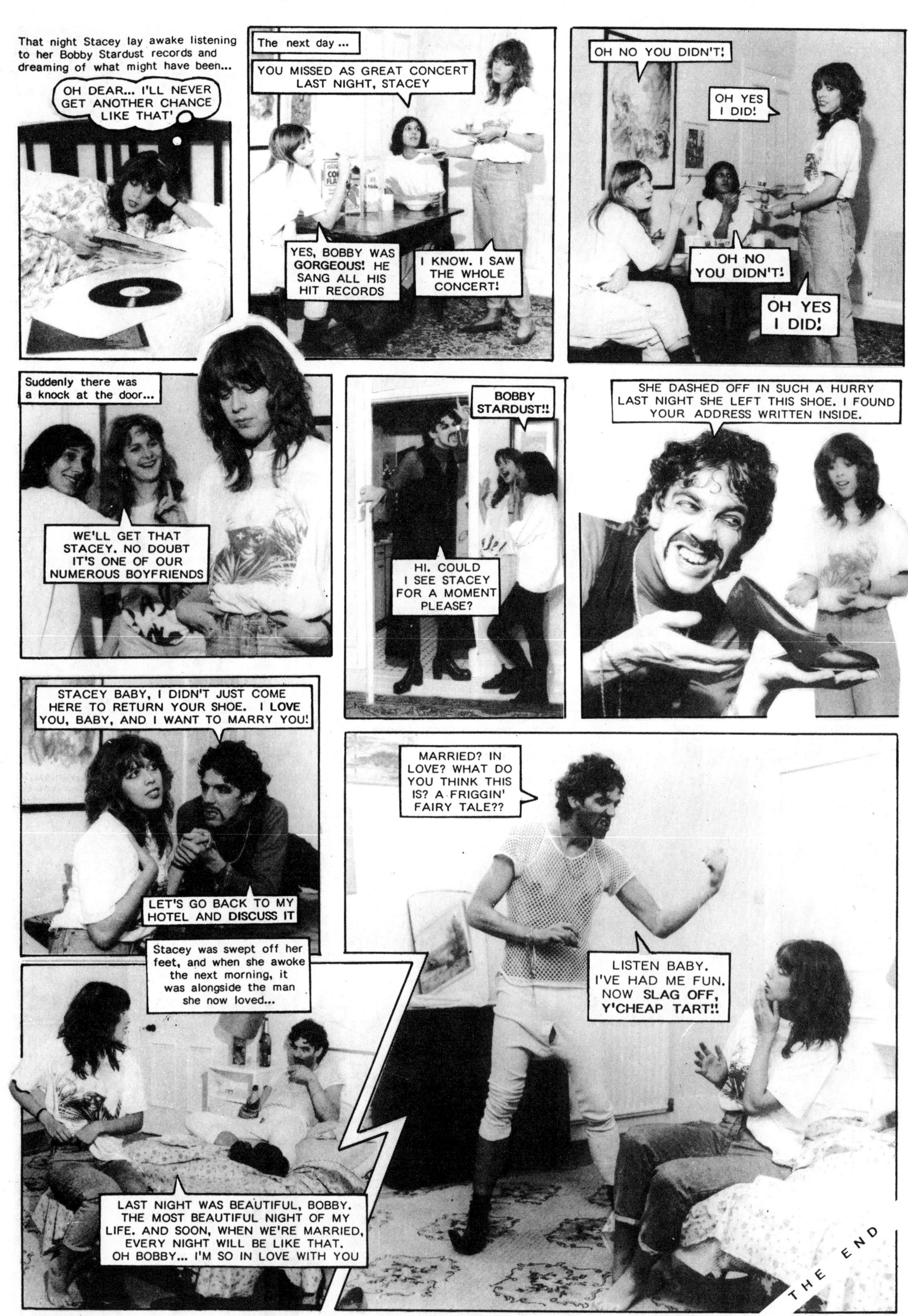


CD/GPD Photography by Colin Davison

# Billy Quizz

Billy Quizz
BILLY IS HOME EARLY FROM WORK...
GLENDA...
...AND FRANK FROM NEXT DOOR!!
BILLY!
I DIDN'T EXPECT YOU BACK SO SOON...

OKAY FRANK, FOR TEN POINTS, WHAT ARE YOU DOING IN BED WITH MY WIFE?
NOW TAKE YOUR TIME FRANK...
REMEMBER, YOUR FIRST ANSWER IS THE ONLY ONE I CAN ACCEPT

I'M SORRY BILL... BUT GLENDA AND I ARE HAVING AN AFFAIR
I SEE. IT'S LIKE THAT IS IT?
IT IS
AND HAS THIS BEEN GOING ON LONG?
IT HAS

BEHIND MY BACK!?
THAT'S CORRECT

TELL ME FRANK - DO YOU LOVE HER?
YES BILLY. I DO
DONG!!
I'M SORRY FRANK...
BUT YOU SAID 'YES' WITH ONLY 15 SECONDS TO GO ON THE CLOCK

RIGHT! LET'S SEE WHERE THAT LEAVES YOU ON THE MASTER SCOREBOARD
SHALL WE FRANK
MASTER SCOREBOARD
POSTMAN 1'20"
GEORGE 47"
MILKMAN 20"
DUSTMAN 10"
BARRY 7"
LIONEL 2"
YOU'RE IN FOURTH PLACE, JUST BEHIND THE MILKMAN

LOOK GLENDA, I THINK I'D BETTER GO. I'LL CALL YOU LATER
NOT SO FAST FRANK!!

YOU'RE NOT GOING TO LEAVE HERE TONIGHT EMPTY HANDED!
UH?
'WAKE UP TO A PIPING HOT CUP OF TEA EVERY MORNING WITH THIS DELIGHTFUL GOBLIN TEASMADE! AN ATTRACTIVE ADDITION TO ANY BEDSIDE TABLE'

COME OFF IT BILL, DON'T BE SILLY. I DON'T WANT IT
MAYBE YOU'D LIKE TO COME BACK NEXT WEEK AND TRY FOR THE WASHING MACHINE?

OR YOU COULD GAMBLE THE MONEY YOU'VE ALREADY WON AND OPEN THE BOX! YOU COULD WALK AWAY WITH OUR STAR PRIZE - A DREAM HOLIDAY IN THE SUN FOR...
BILL'S OBVIOUSLY VERY UPSET, GLENDA. I THINK IT'S BEST IF I GO NOW

SHORTLY...
BILLY. I WANT TO TALK... ABOUT US

RIGHT! YOU'VE GOT SIXTY SECONDS ON THE SUBJECT OF US... STARTING FROM NOW!
STOP IT BILLY, STOP IT WILL YOU!

BZZZZZZ!!
REPETITION!
I'M AFRAID I'LL HAVE TO STOP YOU THERE. YOU SAID 'STOP IT' TWICE

FOR GOD'S SAKE BILLY, STOP IT. I'VE HAD ENOUGH!
OKAY, OKAY
I'LL STOP!

YOU'RE RIGHT LOVE. WE CAN'T GO ON LIKE THIS. WHAT YOU NEED IS TIME TO THINK THINGS OVER

SO WHY DON'T YOU POP ON THESE HEADPHONES AND STEP INTO THE SOUNDPROOF BOOTH FOR A MOMENT
JUST SIT YOURSELF DOWN MY LOVE AND MAKE YOURSELF COMFORTABLE

YOU HAPPY IN THERE ARE YOU? THAT'S LOVELY. NOW JUST YOU RELAX, AND I'LL COME BACK TO YOU IN A MOMENT MY LOVE
SOUND PROOF BOOTH

SHORTLY...
OKAY, YOU CAN COME OUT NOW GLENDA, BUT PLEASE...
BEFORE WE GO ON, THERE'S ONE THING I HAVE TO KNOW ABOUT YOU AND FRANK

IF FRANK TOOK YOU TO THE CINEMA FOR A TREAT, WHAT KIND OF FILM WOULD HE LIKE TO WATCH?
OH GOD!!
WOULD HE LIKE TO SEE A WESTERN-A COWBOY FILM, WOULD HE LIKE TO SEE A MUSICAL - YOU KNOW, WITH LOTS OF SONGS AND DANCING...

WOULD HE LIKE TO SEE A HORROR FILM, OR DOES HE NOT LIKE GOING TO THE CINEMA AT ALL?
THAT'S IT BILL. I'VE HAD ENOUGH. I'M LEAVING!

I'M GOING TO LIVE WITH FRANK. I THINK IT WILL BE BEST FOR BOTH OF US
NO GLENDA!
NO, PLEASE! YOU CAN'T LEAVE ME!

YOU'RE RIGHT. I'VE BEEN A FOOL. IF YOU STAY, I PROMISE THINGS WILL BE DIFFERENT
FROM NOW ON I'LL DEVOTE MY LIFE TO YOU, NOT TO SILLY T.V. GAME SHOWS

OH BILLY, DO YOU REALLY MEAN THAT?

HA! FOOLED YOU!
BLUFF
THAT'S 2 POINTS TO MY TEAM!

LIVING WITH THEIR LIVES ON THE LINE

# DICING WITH DEA

**Every year millions of pounds of tax payers money is spent safeguarding the Royal Family. Yet despite the constant efforts of police and security services, almost every week one of the Royals throws caution to the wind and risks their neck flying helicopters, playing polo or skiing off the Piste.**

ROYAL SENSATION!

Charles and Di — they live for danger.

Far from being safety conscious, the Royal Family seem to thrive on danger, and a growing number of people fear that sooner or later a member of the monarchy could killed or seriously injured.

### ACCIDENT

The most widely publicised incident was Prince Charles' recent return to the ski slopes so soon after the tragic accident in which a colleague died. According to a former ski guide, the Prince regularly leads his party off the Piste and along precarious cliff edges and goat paths, narrowly avoiding rock falls and avalanches.

### DANGEROUS

"He always seeks out the most dangerous routes", our source told us. "He has even been known to ski blindfolded if he felt that the element of danger was lacking".

### EXCITEMENT

Princess Di gives skiing a miss, finding plenty of excitement back home on the streets of London. Bored with Royal rigmarole and security restrictions, Di loves to go for a drive or a shopping trip unaccompanied by her personal detective. As one Palace insider told us, she regularly gives her bodyguard the slip.

"Often she is allowed to travel alone in her car, with a police escort following close behind. But on one occasion she tried to lose her tail by driving the wrong way up a one way street at 130 mph". There followed a thrilling high speed car chase through central London in which six police cars were badly damaged. Eventually the police cornered her in a car park.

### SPEED

"The only way out was through a narrow alleyway less than five feet wide", our insider told us. "So she revved up her engine, then drove the car at high speed onto a nearby ramp, flipping the car up sideways, before swerving through the alley way on two wheels". Detectives later found the wayward Princess shopping unaccompanied in a nearby fashion boutique.

But for every incident that makes the headlines there are many more that never make the news. Like the time when Prince Charles was dicing with death before he'd even reached the ski slopes. A close friend of the Prince takes up the story.

### LEAPT

"Charles had boarded the cablecar and was on his way up to the mountain top when suddenly he realised he'd forgotten his skis. Rather than wait until the car reached the top, he clambered out of a window onto the roof, hundreds of feet up above an icy ravine and leapt onto a passing car travelling in the opposite direction. He then collected the skis from his hotel room before returning to the mountain in slightly less dramatic fashion".

Randy Andy — hair-raising stunts with his chopper.

Brother Andrew, the Duke of York, gets more than his fair share of excitement as a helicopter pilot in the Navy. A former shipmate of the dashing royal who served with Andrew during the Falklands conflict told us that the Duke was always in the thick of the action.

### MISSILE

"His helicopter would often return from anti-submarine patrols riddled with bullet holes. On one particular occasion a large missile had narrowly missed the Prince and lodged itself in his rotar blades, failing to explode.

Typically, the Prince landed his helicopter safely before carrying the unexploded shell to the Officers Mess. Seconds later the device exploded, and the Prince, his face blackened and his clothes in tatters, celebrated by ordering champagne all round".

Fergie — fat arse

While Andrew finds adventure in the forces, at home the Duchess of York's life is by no means quiet. She spends hours in the air flying helicopters and aeroplanes, often at low level, and occasionally amuses herself by flying under bridges, through tunnels and by 'buzzing' motorway traffic. One lorry driver was in for quite a surprise when he stopped at a motorway service station.

### STUNT

"I got out of my lorry and looked up and there was the Duchess of York's helicopter sitting on the back. She must have landed it on top of my load while I was travelling at over 60 mph. I bought her a cup of tea and a bun and chatted to her for a few minutes before she flew off again. She was very friendly — a lovely person — but it did strike me as a rather dangerous stunt for a person in her position to be attempting".

A typical stunt from the Duchess of York — "buzzing" guests at a Palace Garden Party.

Daredevil Di performs a crazy motorbike stunt as her anxious police bodyguard looks on.

Even the older Royals occasionally enjoy a brush with danger. Alarm bells were set ringing recently when the Queen Mother disappeared. Security was put on full alert and a massive search was launched, but after two days police and security services could find no trace of the popular Royal. It was feared that she may have been the victim of a terrorist kidnapping, until news came through that she'd been found — safe and well — by potholers exploring caverns hundreds of feet below the Derbyshire Peaks.

Queen Mum — potholing at 89

The plucky Royal Gran had set off on a solo potholing expedition and become trapped in a narrow fissure hundreds of feet below ground level. With oxygen in short supply, she was fortunate to be rescued in the nick of time by a team of amateur potholers who had been exploring the same area.

### BRAVADO

Relieved relatives threw a party to celebrate her narrow escape and served up a right Royal banquet. Warned by her doctors to avoid fish bones, with typical bravado the Queen Mum tucked into a hearty meal of smoked kippers before downing several pints of stout. An official Palace spokesman explained her disappearance by claiming that the Queen Mother had been 'resting' at Balmoral, the Royal's Scottish holiday retreat.

### BATTLE

A leading psychologist Dr Franz Klausman, believes that the Royal Family's affinty for danger is an inherited condition. "It's in their blood", he told us. "In years gone by Kings and Queens would lead their armies into battle. Nowadays we expect them to to just sit around, wave at people and open things. It's only natural for them to channel their excess energies into exciting and often dangerous pursuits".

### HAZARDOUS

But the Queen fails to agree and she is known to be unhappy at the growing level of disregard for personal safety. Quite rightly she feels that as heirs to the throne her family should be more careful and think twice before partaking in hazardous pursuits. Indeed, only recently she stepped in to block a birthday treat which Charles and Diana had planned for their second son Harry.

### BARREL

The danger loving duo had planned to send the toddler — third in line to the throne — over Niagra Falls in a wooden barrel. But the Queen intervened, claiming that the spectacular stunt was simply too dangerous.

● Opinion - p.27

# Terrace trendies

**A new breed of soccer hooligan — dressed in £800 suits and drinking bubbly at fifty quid a bottle — is replacing the traditional soccer thug.**

## Football thugs who dress to kill

And you won't catch them wearing scarves, hats or Doctor Marten boots. Instead the new yuppie yobs sport dapper suits by Giorgio Armani. Lager is out too. The new generation of louts quaff Dom Perignon champagne by the crate full. No expense is spared. Unlike their predecessors the terrace trouble makers of today hold down highly paid jobs in the City.

### FLICK KNIVES

Flick knives are replaced by filofaxes. The new breed of thug is highly organised. And tattoos are frowned upon. A diamond encrusted Cartier wristwatch is more in keeping with the new image.

### MACHETE

With their £250 hand stitched Jermyn Street silk shirts, you won't catch these thugs 'putting the boot in'. They wouldn't want to risk chaffing their made-to-order Italian pig skin brogues, at £300 a pair.

### SAMURAI SWORD

And it isn't their style to look for trouble. Indeed with their £500 leather Gucci ties, they don't go to football matches at all. Instead they go out, in their solid gold Dunhill cufflinks and Chinchilla socks at £900 a pair, and eat nouvelle cuisine in fasionable restaurants, or just stay at home in their £2 million converted dockland warehouses, relaxing and listening to their £3000 top-of-the-range Nakamichi CD players, with quadraphonic sound.

● Opinion - p.27

# Queen sex

**Members of pop group Queen have taken part in '2-in-a-bed' sex romps with their wives. The saucy stars were believed to be naked at the time.**

**Other pop stars, among them Paul McCartney, are also thought to have had sex with their wives.**

## OLD LADIES

*If you don't pay your gas bill this winter*

**YOU'RE GOING TO PRISON**

**The Gas Board**

*We'll get our fucking bit – don't you worry*

# Cheese blow

**Cheese prices are set to soar. And a pound of Edam could set housewives back as much as £28 a pound if new EEC Cheese Regulations come into effect later this year.**

### TINNED PEAS

**This comes as a double blow to shoppers already reeling from the news that tinned peas are to be outlawed under new Vegetable legislation.**

**Housewife Mrs Vera Wells described the news as "typical". However, there was some consolation for shoppers. A change in the laws governing nuts could mean a drop in the price of chopped almonds. Only a small reduction can be expected, however a saving of between 1 and 2p a pound could be passed on to housewives.**

# Billy the Fish

FULCHESTER UNITED, IN THE DOLDRUMS SINCE THE DEATH OF BILLY THOMSON, HAVE BEEN UNSUCCESSFUL IN THEIR ATTEMPTS TO FIND A REPLACEMENT FOR THE LATE 'FISH-LIKE' KEEPER.

NON-LEAGUE NO-HOPERS SUDLEY LANE PAPERBOYS ELEVEN, VERSUS FULCHESTER UNITED...

THAT'S JUST THE KIND OF DRAW I WAS HOPING FOR, SYD.

BUT WHAT ARE WE GOING TO DO FOR A KEEPER, BOSS? THE GAME KICKS OFF IN LESS THAN 24 HOURS.

DON'T WORRY SYD. AGAINST A BUNCH OF AMATEURS WE SHOULDN'T NEED ONE!

COME ON SYD! GIVE ME A HAND UP!
OOF!
FUFC

HEY MISTER! CAN WE HAVE OUR BALL BACK?

WELL BOSS. DID YOU GET IT?

NO SYD. HE'S BUST IT.

WHAT DO WE DO NOW? WE CAN'T CARRY ON WITHOUT A BALL. IT WOULD MAKE A MOCKERY OF THE GAME!
UM FIASCO.
EXCUSE ME!

YOU CAN USE MY BALL IF YOU LIKE. BUT ONLY ON ONE CONDITION...

...THAT I GET A GAME!

WE'VE GOT NO CHOICE, SYD. WE'LL HAVE TO GIVE THE YOUNG BALLBOY WILLY THOMSON A GAME.
I SUPPOSE SO.
WE MAY AS WELL STICK HIM IN GOAL. HE CAN'T DO MUCH HARM THERE.

OKAY SONNY - YOU'RE IN THE GOAL.
WHY THANK-YOU MR. BROWN SIR. I WON'T LET YOU DOWN.

IT ISN'T LONG UNTIL UNITED ARE ON THE ATTACK AGAIN...
A FANTASTIC TURN OF SPEED FROM THE BUXOM YET FLEET-FOOTED REDSKIN WINGER!

BROWN FOX IS CERTAINLY SCYTHING THROUGH THE SUDLEY LINES OF DEFENCE LIKE A TOMAHAWK.
YES. SHE'S SHOWING ALL THE "ON THE BALL" ABILITIES OF HER FOREFATHERS.

BUT...
A HOPELESSLY WIDE KICK BY THE REDSKIN!
UGH! UM HEAP BAD TOE-ENDER!
YES. THAT WILL SURELY DISPLEASE HOTAN-TANKA - THE CHEROKEE GOD OF SOCCER.

WE'RE CREATING THE CHANCES, SYD, BUT WE'RE NOT DOING THE DAMAGE WHERE IT MATTERS - IN THEIR EIGHTEEN YARD AREA.
HMMM.

SEVERAL HOURS LATER...
IT'S BECOMING INCREASINGLY DIFFICULT TO SEE THE BALL.
YES. IT MUST BE GETTING LATE BY NOW.
I WONDER WHAT TIME IT IS.

HAS ANYONE GOT A WATCH?
NO.
NOPE.
SORRY.

BUT IF NOBODY'S KEEPING TIME - HOW WILL WE KNOW WHEN TO END THE GAME?
THAT'S A GOOD QUESTION, BOSS.

LET'S ASK OUR MIDFIELD SCIENTIFIC SPECIALIST, PROFESSOR WÖLFGANG SCHNELL BSc. PhD. PERHAPS HE CAN BRING HIS ENORMOUS INTELLECT TO BEAR ON THE PROBLEM.

AH. ZE PROBLEM HERE IS EIN LOGICAL ONE. YOU SEE, UNLIKE SPACE, TIME IS EIN ABSTRACT CONCEPT - AND ZEREFORE DOES NOT FOLLOW THE EUCLIDEAN RULES OF LOGIC. EVEN IF WE LOOK AT IT MATHEMATICALLY, WE LACK ZE NECESSARY INTEGER, ie ZE PRECISE TIME OF KICK-OFF. THUS, EVEN NOTVISSTANDINK KNOWLEDGE OF ZE PRESENT TIME, ZE DURATION OF PLAY IS IMPOSSIBLE TO CALCULATE.
ZE SOLUTION TO ZIS PROBLEM, ZEREFORE, LIES ALSO IN ZE ABSTRACT, RATHER THAN ZE CONCRETE, OR LOGICAL, DIMENSION.

TO CONCLUDE, I ZEREFORE HYPOTHESISE - NEXT GOAL'S ZE WINNER, JA?
FINE REASONING UNDER PRESSURE THERE FROM THE BALDING TEUTON

BUT, WITH THE MATCH DELICATELY POISED IN A SUDDEN-DEATH CLIFF-HANGING SITUATION...
SUDLEY HAVE BROKEN FORWARD!
OH NO!

HE'S ONLY GOT THE KEEPER TO BEAT!
AND REMEMBER, A SINGLE SUDLEY GOAL WILL LEAVE FULCHESTER'S F.A. CUP HOPES DASHED!
YES.
CAN YOUNG WILLY "BILLY" THOMSON SAVE THE DAY - AND KEEP HIS TEAM'S F.A. CUP HOPES ALIVE? DON'T MISS THE NEXT EPISODE!!

# QUEEN HITS BACK!

**WORLD EXCLUSIVE**

## 'Anyone who says my job's easy is talking out their arse'

**Over the years the Royal Family have been criticised for being overpaid, over priviliged and out of date. Yet no matter how vicious the attacks, the Royals have always remained silent, steadfastly refusing to answer their critics.**

Buckimgan Palace,
London.

Dear Sir

I am bloody furious, me. So I think its about time you and t
exackthy
about al
what peo
me and al

I'dont have to pay (I'm the bloody Queen!)

The Editor
Viz
P.O. Box 1 PT
Newcastle.

TO PAY 12p

### ROYAL MAIL

**On Her Majesty's Service—The Royal letter which was delivered to our offices by the postman yesterday.**

But now, for the first time ever the Queen has decided to break her silence and **HIT BACK** at her knockers. In an astonishing frank and forthright letter to this paper she has revealed exclusively **THE TRUTH** about life in the Royal Family. Here, in the first extract from her remarkable letter, the Queen puts the record straight about **MONEY** and the Royals.

**The Queen at work yesterday**

### PAYMENT

We would like to make it clear that the Queen has received no payment or fee from us, nor has she benefited in any other way financially from the publication of this letter.

### BILLS

'People think I'm rolling in it, cos I'm the Queen. But once I've paid the bills an' that I've hardly got enough left to see me through the week. As often as not by Friday I'm on the scrounge.

### PEANUTS

I get dead mad when people say "Aaah! Look at her. I bet she's coining it in". That's rubbish. You wouldn't believe the number of times I've had to go hundreds of miles to open a building or something, and I've been paid nowt. Even if they do decide to cough up a few bob, it's usually peanuts. At the end of the day I'm lucky if I come away with enough to cover me train fare.

### FORTUNE

I had to open a bridge the other day. Of course the punters expect me to look the part — it's more than my jobs worth to be seen wearing the same hat twice. And posh frocks don't come cheap either. I spent a bleedin' fortune on a new outfit, and all I got for opening the bridge was a "Thank You Your Majesty". Try giving that to the bank manager.

### NAPPIES

Don't get me wrong. I'm not just doing this for the money. There's easier ways of making a living than this, I can tell you. Opening things and waving at people is no picnic. I should know — I've been in this game over fifty years. I was opening buildings when Princess Di was still in nappies, but nowadays it's her and Fergie what get the headlines. I'm not kidding, them two probably get paid ten times as much as I do. Me, the Queen, and them just Princesses 'n all. I sometimes wonder why I bother.

### FLACK

Whenever people slag off the Royals, it's always me what takes the flack. I don't care what they say — I do a rudy good job. For instance, if I'm booked to open something, I'm always there on time, looking the part. I don't mess around. I smile, I meet people an' that, and when it comes to speeches I do a bloody good turn — at least twenty minutes, and no boring bits either. Not like the young 'uns. They turn up in their helicopters, smile for the telly then 'woosh!' They're off on holiday again. I can't remember the last time me and Phil had a decent holiday. We're lucky if we get a weekend off all year. Take it from me, anyone who says my job is easy is talking out their arse.

## HM blasts the armchair critics

### STAMPS

For instance, I never get a minute to myself during the day, and there's no chance of going out in the evening for a quiet drink or a meal in a posh restaurant. People see me all the time on money and stamps, and once they've recognised me they just won't leave me alone.

In the old days you got a bit of respect. We had a few bob back then 'n all. In them days if we had a banquet we used to put on a really good spread. Out would come the silver, there'd be seven or eight courses, with caviar, champagne, posh mints. The works. These days if someone like the King of France comes over he's lucky if he gets a bowl of soup before the main course. And more often than not there isn't even a choice of puddings.

### POP STARS

I'm not one to grumble. After all, there's always thems what's worse off than yourself. But when you see the amount of money that pop stars and the like are making these days, it makes you wonder. You'd expect someone like the Queen would be taken care of. After all, being the Queen's not something I do for the good of me health you know.

In the next issue: How I hit the roof when I found out Fergie was pregnant. Plus them Royal Weddings — what a pain in the arse.'

OH, DEAR, I DON'T FANCY YOURS MUCH... IT'S THE

# FAT SLAGS

OVER MY DEAD BODY
I'M WARNING YOU. THIS IS YOUR TWELVTH AND FINAL CHANCE! HOW ABOUT IT, EH? I PROMISE I DON'T BITE!
I'M SORRY KEITH. I CAN'T. I'M BUSY TONIGHT.
Every time Keith Parker asked pretty Michelle Thomson for a date, the answer seemed to be 'no' ...

YOU'RE **ALWAYS** BUSY. YOU NEVER GO OUT AND ENJOY YOURSELF. PERHAP'S I'M JUST NOT YOUR TYPE, IS THAT IT?
OH KEITH, IT'S NOT THAT. I REALLY LIKE YOU ...

BUT IT'S MY MOTHER. SHE WON'T LET ME GO OUT IN THE EVENINGS. I'M SORRY KEITH. I'D LIKE TO SEE YOU, BUT I CAN'T.
ALRIGHT THEN, BUT I'M WARNING YOU. I DON'T GIVE UP THAT EASILY!

Inside ...
WHO WAS THAT YOU WERE TALKING TO OUTSIDE?
OH, THAT WAS KEITH — THAT NICE BOY I TOLD YOU ABOUT. ACTUALLY, I WAS WONDERING WHETHER I COULD ...

SO, HE'S A **MAN** IS HE?
I'VE TOLD YOU BEFORE. YOU'RE NOT TO GET INVOLVED WITH MEN. NEVER, DO YOU HEAR ME? **NEVER!!**

NOW GO TO YOUR ROOM AND STAY THERE FOR THE REST OF THE EVENING!
YES MOTHER.
MEN INDEED!

IT'S NOT FAIR. MOTHER HATES MEN JUST BECAUSE DADDY LEFT HER TO BRING ME UP ALONE. SHE'S CONVINCED ALL MEN ARE THE SAME, BUT THEY'RE NOT. IF ONLY SHE'D GIVE KEITH A CHANCE.
The next morning ...
HEY MICHELLE! GUESS WHAT!
I'VE GOT TWO TICKETS TO SEE WET WET WET AT THE TOWN HALL TONIGHT. FANCY IT?

OH KEITH ... YOU KNOW I CAN'T.
HEY, COME ON. I MAY NOT BE AS GOOD LOOKING AS MARTI PELLOW, BUT I CAN PROMISE YOU A FUN NIGHT OUT!
I'M SORRY KEITH.

MICHELLE. YOU'RE SEVENTEEN. YOU CAN'T GO ON LIVING IN YOUR MOTHER'S SHADOW FOREVER. YOU HAVE YOUR OWN LIFE TO LIVE.
ENJOY YOURSELF FOR A CHANGE. DON'T WORRY ABOUT YOUR MOTHER. SHE'LL SOON COME ROUND TO YOUR WAY OF THINKING. TRUST ME.
YOU'RE RIGHT KEITH, THIS IS **MY** LIFE.
I **WILL** GO TO THE CONCERT WITH YOU. I'D LOVE TO!
I DON'T BELIEVE IT! SHE FINALLY SAID 'YES'. THIRTEENTH TIME LUCKY!
But early that evening when Michelle broke the news to her mother ...
A POP CONCERT ... WITH A **MAN? OVER MY DEAD BODY.** YOU LITTLE TRAMP. YOU'LL DO NO SUCH THING, DO YOU HEAR ME?
MOTHER, I'M GOING AND THERE'S NOTHING YOU CAN DO TO STOP ME.
IF YOU GET INTO THAT CAR I'LL KILL MYSELF!
I'M WARNING YOU, YOUNG GIRL. I'LL **KILL MYSELF**, DO YOU HEAR ME?
TAKE NO NOTICE OF HER. SHE DOES'NT MEAN IT. COME ON, LET'S GO FOR A COFFEE BEFORE THE SHOW.
YEAH, I THINK I NEED ONE.
Shortly ...
HEY! IT MAY NEVER HAPPEN! COME ON, YOU'RE SUPPOSED TO BE HAVING FUN. YOU LOOK LIKE DEATH WARMED UP!
IT'S MY MOTHER. I'M REALLY WORRIED THAT SHE'LL DO SOMETHING STUPID.
ALRIGHT! I GIVE UP! WE'LL GO BACK AND SEE YOUR MOTHER. I NEVER REALLY LIKED THE WETS MUCH ANYWAY.
I'M SORRY KEITH. YOU MUST BE SICK OF ME.
DON'T WORRY ABOUT ME. I'M HAVING A WONDERFUL TIME!

Photography by Colin D. CD/GPD 12.88 Special thanks to Jean.

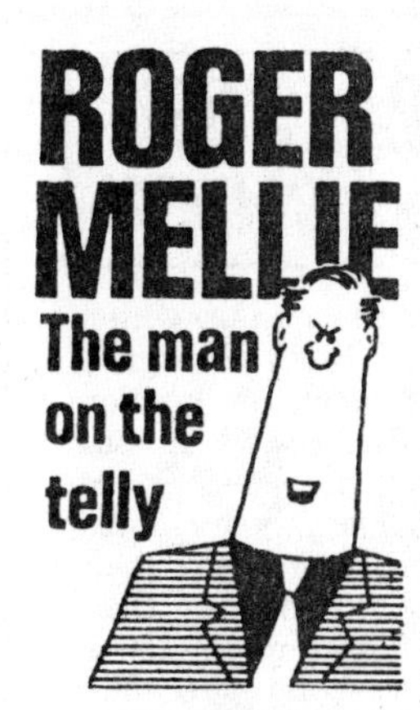
ROGER MELLIE
The man on the telly

F.T.V. HAVE AN IMPORTANT VISITOR...
I'M SURE YOU'LL FIND HERE AT F.T.V. OUR PROGRAMMES ARE MADE WITH A FAMILY AUDIENCE VERY MUCH IN MIND
THAT'S MOST COMMENDABLE
AND IN THE COMING YEAR I BELIEVE WE ARE INCREASING OUR BUDGET FOR RELIGIOUS AND EDUCATIONAL PROGRAMMES BY TEN PER CENT

HEY TOM! HOW ABOUT THIS FOR A NEW GAME SHOW... 'UP YOUR CUNT!'

IT'S BRILLIANT. THREE CELEBRITIES ALL GIVE A DIFFERENT DEFINITION OF A WORD, AND IF THE AUDIENCE THINK THEY'RE LYING, THEY ALL SHOUT "UP YOUR CUNT!"
OH GOD, NO!

ERM... YES ROGER. WE'LL TALK ABOUT IT LATER, EH?
IT'S A WINNER TOM

LOOK ROGER. YOU'LL HAVE TO EXCUSE ME. I'M JUST ABOUT TO TAKE MY GUEST OUT TO LUNCH
OOOH, LUNCH EH? GREAT! I'M FUCKIN' STARVIN'

NO ROGER, HADN'T YOU BETTER BE FINISHING THOSE NEWS REPORTS? WE NEED THEM BY THREE
AAH, FUCK THEM TOM. I'M GASPING FOR A PINT!

I DO APOLOGIZE FOR THIS INTRUSION. ROGER HAS BEEN WITH US FOR SEVERAL YEARS. A FIRST RATE PRESENTER, DESPITE HIS OCCASIONAL ECCENTRICITIES!
SO ANYWAY, THIS SHOW, RIGHT? WE'LL GET ALL THE BIG NAMES - TARBY, BOB, BRUCEY AND... ER... WHAT'S 'ER NAME... YOU KNOW. THE BIRD WITH BIG TITS

AT THE RESTAURANT...
...THEN THE CONTESTANT HAS TO NAME SIX KINDS OF FISH BEFORE THE STRIPPER GETS HER KIT OFF. IF HE DOES HE WINS THE CAR. FUCKING GREAT EH TOM?
I THINK WE'D BETTER ORDER NOW ROGER
Menu

HEY GARCON! CAN WE HAVE A FEW BOTTLES OF WINE OVER HERE, PRONTO. WHAT DO YOU FANCY, RED OR WHITE? I'LL HAVE A LARGE WHITE
HOW ABOUT YOU TOM?

FUCK ME! HAVE YOU SEEN THE PRICES!?

HEY! WHO'S PAYING TOM? YOU OR YOUR MATE
FOR HEAVEN'S SAKE, KEEP YOUR VOICE DOWN ROGER!

SOON...
SO ANYWAY, WHAT'S YOUR GAME EH? IN THE TELLY BUSINESS ARE YOU?
YOU COULD SAY THAT
MR HOGG IS FROM THE GOVERNMENT'S NEW T.V. MONITORING COMMITTEE, ROGER. HE'S BEEN CHECKING UP ON US TODAY.

OH RIGHT! YOU'RE THE LUCKY SOD WHO GETS TO WATCH ALL THE PORNO VIDEOS THEN, EH?
DON'T BE RIDICULOUS

GO ON TOM, TELL HIM WHAT IT WAS LIKE
AHEM! NOT NOW ROGER!

HEY, I SAW ONE LAST WEEK, IT WOULD HAVE MADE YOUR HAIR CURL! TALK ABOUT HOT STUFF. YOU HAVE NEVER SEEN ANYTHING LIKE THIS!
I'M SURE MR HOGG DOESN'T WISH TO KNOW ABOUT YOUR PORNOGRAPHIC VIDEO, AND FRANKLY NIETHER DO I

HEY, HONESTLY, IT'S SHIT HOT I CAN GET YOU A COPY IF YOU LIKE
NO THANKYOU MR MELLIE

THE PURPOSE OF MY VISIT TODAY HAS BEEN TO ASSESS THE MORAL AND PROFESSIONAL STANDARDS BEING MAINTAINED BY YOUR COMPANY, AS WELL AS THE STANDARD OF THE PROGRAMMES BEING SHOWN
AND I AM FAR FROM HAPPY WITH WHAT I HAVE FOUND

IN ALL MY YEARS I HAVE NEVER COME ACROSS ANYONE AS VULGAR, UNPROFESSIONAL AND TOTALLY INEPT AS YOURSELF MR MELLIE
OH FUCK. IS THIS ONE EMPTY?
FRANKLY, YOUR BEHAVIOUR DISGUSTS ME!

I HAVE NO CHOICE OTHER THAN TO RECOMMEND THAT F.T.V.'S LICENSE BE SUSPENDED INDEFINITELY!
I'LL TRY SOME OF THIS
GOOD DAY TO YOU!

WHAT'S UP WITH HIM? DAFT SOD. ANYWAY, AS I WAS SAYING TOM, 'UP YOUR CUNT' - IT'S AN ABSOLUTE WINNER!
DROP MORE WINE?
CD. GPD. 89

## SMASH! BANG! WALLOP! It's the page that packs CLOUT!

## Terrorists have gone too far

This consumer terrorism has gone to far. First it was glass in pet food, then fuse wire in baby food. And now while eating my cornflakes this morning I almost choked on a small plastic dinosaur.

What will these callous people think of next?

S. Jones
York

My neighbour and I share the same surname — Brown — and this often leads to confusion. In order to solve the problem I suggested that he change his name to something more distinctive, such as Titmouse or Sidebottom. However he refused.
Do any other readers have awkward neighbours?

Mr. B. Brown
Weymouth

The problem with unemployed people these days is that they don't want to work.

Mrs. P. Hartington,
Tunbridge Wells

## They're at it again

Surprise, surprise. These so called "green do gooders" are at it again. Now they tell us we can't shoot elephants! Well, that's all well and good, but will they kindly tell us where we're supposed to get our ivory from? It doesn't grow on trees you know. Perhaps if they took a few less drugs, they'd be able to think straight.

Major Percy Reid
Hexborough

I thought my luck was in the day a pretty girl approached me in the pub and asked if I could get her a drink. Then I remembered — I was serving behind the bar at the time.

Tony Noble
Burnley

## Good turn turns sour

My son, who is unemployed, decided to weed our next door neighbour's garden in order to pass the time. To his surprise, our delighted neighbour handed him a £10 note for his trouble. A most generous gesture.

Naturally my son was over the moon — until the next day when a police officer called and arrested him. He'd forgotten that I work for the DHSS, and had promptly reported him for carrying on paid work while claiming benefit.

Mr. A. Douglas
Buxton

My husband came up with a great idea to beat the burglars when we went on holiday recently. He locked up our house then nipped over the wall into our neighbours garden and prized open one of their windows, thus making their house a far more attractive proposition to burglars than our own!

Mrs. M. Woodward
Gillingham

## Identical car mix-up

My car is practically identical to my neighbours. I thought I had solved the problem the other day when I had a sun roof fitted to mine. However I arrived home only to find that my neighbour had done exactly the same thing!

At last I think I solved the problem. Last night I went out into the street and broke my neighbours windscreen and headlights with a garden spade.

D. Ashcroft
Wigan

## TOP TIPS

**STAND your cooker on a tea chest. This prevents young children reaching the hot areas, and provides useful storage space for busy mums.**

**Curly Lox
Glastonbury**

**USE talcum powder on cakes instead of icing sugar. It is not fattening and it's much kinder to teeth.**

**Mis. J. Holland
Southfields**

**SAVE money on expensive hair gel. Marmalade makes a cheap substitute, but beware of bees in the summer.**

**M. Boyle
Surrey**

**STRETCH a piece of elastic and make marks at 1 inch intervals and 'Hey Presto' — a telescopic ruler which takes up very little room in a handbag or pocket. By stretching it to different degrees it can easily be converted from imperial to metric measures.**

**A. Kinloch
Harringay**

**POP a few teabags in your hot water tank and you can make a hot cuppa anytime, by just turning on the tap.**

**Mrs. M. Growitt
Birmingham**

**ANNOY traffic wardens by knocking their hats off.**

**Mr. I. Woods
Bolton**

**AVOID drink/driving by drinking so much alcohol that by closing time you have completely forgotten ever having owned a car.**

**Mike Grey
Essex**

**FIND your way to the toilet in the dark by tying a length of string from the bowl to the toilet door. Simply straddle the string and slide the cleft of your buttocks along the string until you feel the toilet seat touch your genitals. Simple.**

**S. Jeames
Brighton**

**PREVENT thieves stealing the crooklock from your car by attaching one end to the steering wheel and the other to one of the pedals.**

**D. Marshall (Mr.)
Stockton-on-Tees**

**REMOVE all the buttons from articles of clothing before putting them in the washing machine. This prevents them making a clanking noise against the glass.**

**Mrs. I. Graham
Berkshire**

**TAKE your dustbin with you to the supermarket so that you can see which items you have recently run out of.**

**S. Elliot
London**

**INCREASE the life of your carpets by rolling them up and storing them in the garage.**

**A. Allied
S. Wales**

**WHENEVER you're shot in the chest, lie on the side you were hit. That way, only one lung will fill with blood.**

**Major G. Symonds
Codsall**

**WHEN boarding a bus, avoid payment of your fare by trying to pretend that you are with the person in front of you.**

**I. Peters
Gravesend**

**CONVINCE your postman that you are more popular than you actually are by sending yourself several hundred Christmas cards each year.**

**T. James
Huddersfield**

**AVOID being engaged in 'polite' conversation with total strangers on buses by pretending to be drunk.**

**Trevor Williams
Woolwich**

**PAINT the windows of your car black in order to enjoy the advantages of night-time driving throughout the day.**

**P. Murray
Hampstead**

**CONFUSE your milkman by ordering one pint of milk each day, then buying a dozen extra pints from a nearby shop, thus leaving thirteen empty bottles on the doorstep every morning.**

**Mrs. P. Wilkinson
Hemel Hempstead**

# SEX IN THE YEAR 2000

**Have you ever imagined what it will be like to have sex in the future? Will space-age sex be different to the way we make love today? Experts believe it will. Indeed a 21st century sex revolution could change the way we live. So let's take a look into the future and look forward to having SEX IN THE YEAR 2000.**

Over the years, attitudes towards sex have changed dramatically. Well, those attitudes will continue to change. By the year 2000 Victorian values will be a thing of the past. Gone will be inhibitions and prudish attitudes towards sex. Instead making love will seem as natural as lighting a cigarette — strangers will do it at bus stops, on trains or where-ever the fancy takes them.

### SEX

The out-dated Indecent Behaviour laws will have been removed from the statute books — instead the police will actively encourage people to make love. Sex will be so common-place, our clothes will be specially adapted so there's no need to take them off when we have sex.

### SEXUAL

At work, coffee and tea breaks will be replaced by sex breaks. Bosses, following the Japanese example, will realise that sexual stimulation increases productivity. Profits will be up, and Britain will boom to the sound of bonking.

### SEXY

New healthy attitudes towards the subject of sex will mean the end of seedy sex shops. Instead families will visit huge out-of-town sex hypermarkets, with free parking for over 2000 cars, selling everything you could ever need for sex. From sexy underwear to a pair of skimpy briefs. And sex hypermarkets will be open on bank holidays too!

Sex will no longer be an awkward, old-fashioned show of affection between two people that takes place behind closed doors. People will have sex at all times of the day, in all sorts of places, and in any numbers. At football matches whole crowds will have sex together to celebrate a goal. And new attitudes will mean no more complaints about sex on TV. Instead, old ladies will sit down and enjoy the Eurovision Sex Contest. A grey-haired Terry Wogan will present the show, and couples from all over Europe will have sex on screen, hoping to win the competition. Indeed, competitive sex will be the sport of the future with top athletes, at the peak of their physical fitness, going for gold in sex — the most popular olympic sport of the year 2000.

Incredible advances in technology will begin to change sex beyond all recognition. As well as Access and Visa, people will eventually carry SexExpress cards. To have sex with other SexExpress cardholders, simply pop the card into any High Street SexPoint machine . At the end of the month you will receive a statement letting you know how many times you have had sex, and with whom.

### SEXINESS

Cinemas will have been replaced by multi-screen Sexi-mas. Having sex with your favourite movie star will become a reality, thanks to special attachments on the seat in front of you. Meanwhile at home watching TV will never be the same again. Special hologramic TVs will allow you to have sex with the newsreader as they read the headlines, or fondle your favourite weatherman as he makes his forecast.

And new technology will also make sex possible via the phone. Simply ring a friend's number, then plug your telephone into a special socket in your bed. Crossed lines could lead to some thrilling threesomes, or even a fabulous foursome. But beware — these sexiphone sessions are likely to cost you as much as £600 per minute at peak times, owing to inflation.

### SEXUALITY

Sex education will be revolutionised too. The children of the future will learn sex in the classroom along with English and maths. They will be able to visit Sex Museums too, where actors will perform old-fashioned "bedroom sex" — the kind we enjoy today. By the year 2000, sex in bed will be a thing of the past.

### SEXTANT

Sexual diseases will also be a thing of the past. Doctors will have invented a special new space medicine that tastes like lemonade and stops you from catching any sex diseases. And pregnancy will not be a problem either. Women will be able to swallow a special pill every night, smaller than a smartie, and if taken regularly this will stop them becoming pregnant.

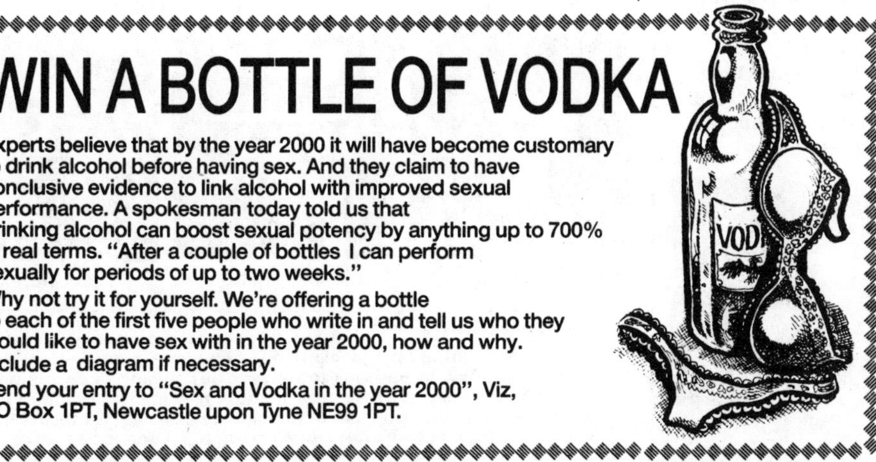

# A RIGHT ROYAL

## Who would they turn to for Royal rumpy pumpy?

**We all love and respect the Royal Family. Their impeccable behaviour is a shining example to us all. For this reason we find recent press speculation surrounding the private lives of certain Royals totally contemptable. In marriage as in other things the Royals exercise the highest moral standards, and we would never dare to suggest otherwise.**

But the Royals are only human. And who are we to say that there could not conceivably be an adulterer among them? And if they were to temporarily stray from marital fidelity, where would they turn for a bit of royal rumpy pumpy?

Just for fun, we asked a leading sex expert to assess each member of the Royal Family and to tell us what sort of person they would most likely turn to for a quick roll on the red carpet.

For each Royal he has named three nookie nominees. Strictly for fun, use your knowledge of sex and the Royals to select who you think are the most likely candidates. When you've finished compare your choices with those of our expert which are written below.

## PRINCESS DIANA

One of Di's main interests is fashion and clothes — of all the Royals she is definately the most daring when it comes to dressing up. She would therefore have a great deal in common with pop star **BOY GEORGE**. Significantly Di also has a genuine interest in the rehabilitation of drug victims.

A former nanny and now mother of two, Di has a great deal of affection for children. Perhaps a fling with poncy choir boy **ALED JONES** would bring out the mother in her.

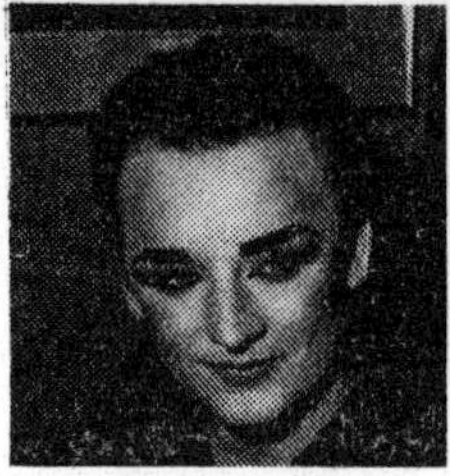
Star George

Aled: Choirboy

D.J. Fluff

Alternatively Di's other great interest — pop music — may lead her towards a lover in the music world. Somebody like top DJ **ALAN FREEMAN**, who could no doubt impress her with a wide and varied record collection.

## PRINCE CHARLES

Charles has many varied interests. Among them sport, painting and writing children's books. But he is also renowned for his strong interest in architecture, where he has a preference for old, classical styles rather than anything new or unusual. For this reason I believe he'd be attracted to a more mature woman, conservative in her appearance. **MARGARET THATCHER** is just such a woman, and therefore a likely candidate.

In an affair Charles would also be looking for a change — something different. His wife, Princess Di is a slim, elegant lady. So perhaps he'd be attracted to the contrasting, stocky, athletic figure of **FATIMA WHITBREAD** who he has no doubt met during official visits to athletic events.

Finally, Charles made no secret of his admiration for top seventies pop group **THE THREE DEGREES.** Perhaps the thought of a steamy foursome with the attractive american trio would tempt the Prince into adultery.

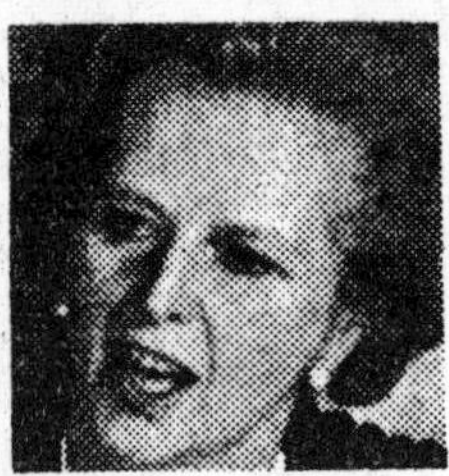
Maggie: Woman

Athlete Fatima

Degrees: Three

## THE QUEEN

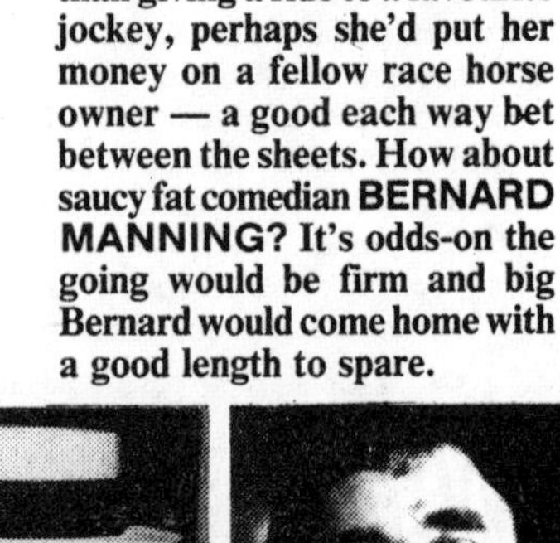

Among the Queen's many interests are art collecting, horse racing and hats. So perhaps it would be from one of these areas that she would select her Royal Romeo. A prominent artist for example, like **ROLF HARRIS**. The Queen has probably heard that he is very big down under.

Perhaps Her Majesty's fondness of flamboyant hats would suggest a shared interest and the possiblity of a rewarding romance with extrovert pop star **ELTON JOHN.** The highly talented singer/songwriter would no doubt derive much satisfaction from tinkling the Queen's ivories.

But maybe the Queen's first love, horse racing could turn up an odds on favourite in the rumpy pumpy stakes. And rather than giving a ride to a favourite jockey, perhaps she'd put her money on a fellow race horse owner — a good each way bet between the sheets. How about saucy fat comedian **BERNARD MANNING?** It's odds-on the going would be firm and big Bernard would come home with a good length to spare.

Rolf: Painter

Elton: Hats

Bernard: Fat

**ANSWERS**

In our expert's opinion if the Royal Family were involved in hanky panky (which obviously they never would be) the pairings would be as follows. Prince Charles and Fatima Whitbread. Princess Di and Aled Jones. Prince Andrew and Joan Collins. The Duchess of York and Dr Magnus Pyke. The Queen and Bernard Manning. The Duke of Edinburgh and Jeanette Krankie. The Queen Mother and Cliff Richard.

# BIT ON THE SIDE

## PRINCE ANDREW

A fully qualified Royal Navy helicopter pilot, Andrew would have an obvious shared interest with former Treasure Hunt presenter, action loving **ANNEKA RICE**.

The Prince has never lived down his "randy Andy" reputation and it may well be that he would prefer a more experienced woman, someone who has been around a bit and is capable of satisfying a vast sexual appetite. For this reason "Stud" actress **JOAN COLLINS** would spring to mind.

Consider also Andrew's known taste in women. In choosng Sarah Ferguson as his bride he revealed an affinity for the more generously proportioned figure. Perhaps for this reason caring heavyweight **CLARE RAYNER** should be considered.

Anneka: Loves choppers

Collins: Stud

Clare: She cares

## PRINCESS FERGIE

Lazenby —'007'

Eddie 'The Eagle'

Pyke: Brainy

Fergie's action packed lifestyle reveals on outgoing, danger loving personality. The flame haired Duchess constantly seeks adventure in the air and on the ski slopes, never content to stay at home and watch TV. The lady lives for thrills and who better to provide these than tough guy James Bond star **GEORGE LAZENBY.**

There is no doubt that of all the Royals Fergie has by far the best opportunities for "hankie pankie". While hubby is away at sea the Duchess spends hours alone on the piste, and perhaps this fascination with winter sports would suggest that an affair with British Olympic ski champion **EDDIE EDWARDS** is on the cards.

Or perhaps she would surprise us all and go for brains instead of brawn. A suave, sophisticated intellectual like **DR MAGNUS PYKE** would make a refreshing change from the hunk in her life, Prince Andy.

## THE DUKE OF EDINBURGH

Unlike the other Royals the Duke has his roots overseas — in Greece to be precise. And he occasionally pines for his native country. Perhaps therefore a steaming affair with fellow Greek **NANA MOUSKOURI** would bring the memories of home flooding back.

Or maybe after a lifetime spent in the shadow of his more famous wife, the Duke may want a woman whom he could dominate physically, someone smaller than himself and with a much lower public profile than the Queen. Someone like top schoolboy impersonator **JEANETTE KRANKIE** would fit that description.

But after being bogged down for so long by Royal rigmorole, etiquette and never ending formalities, maybe the Duke would be tempted to go down market in search of "the common touch". No doubt he'd find an abundance of warmth and sincerity in down to earth bubbly blonde "Carry On" star **BARBARA WINDSOR.**

Songbird Nana

Cuddly Jeanette

Babs: Busty

## THE QUEEN MUM

The Queen Mum would be looking for the companionship that only a true gentleman could give, someone with the grace and charm of generations past. A man with all these qualities is doubtlessly clean cut singer **CLIFF RICHARD.**

Or perhaps the deep, genuine, compassionate tones of attractive yet mature radio disc jockey **SIMON BATES** could win her heart. Doubtless the couple could spend many "golden hours" together.

Or would Britain's best loved great grandmother, now in the autumn of her years, prefer to have a toy boy at her disposal? I'm sure it would do her no harm whatsoever to have a youngster like current pop sensation **JASON DONOVAN** running around the corridors of Clarence house.

Clean-cut Cliff

Bates: Genuine

Jason: Neighbourly

Mrs Brady
OLD LADY.

THERE YOU GO MRS. BRADY- RIGHT OUTSIDE YOUR OWN FRONT DOOR!

MMMF!

GGNNN!
OOOF!
ARE YOU ALRIGHT THERE LOVE? CAN I GIVE YOU A HAND WITH THAT?

YOU CAN TAKE YOUR WANDERING HANDS OFF ME YOUNG MAN, YOU DIRTY ROB DOG. I'M NOT AS GREEN AS I'M CABBAGE LOOKING.
IT'S ME PURSE YOU'RE AFTER.

5 MINUTES LATER...
OOF!
SOME OF US HAVE GOT APPOINTMENTS TO KEEP!
GAH!
struggle struggle
SHE'S DOING IT ON PURPOSE
YES.
THEY'VE GOT ALL WEEK TO DO THEIR SHOPPING.

10 MINUTES LATER...
IF I EVER GET LIKE THAT- WILL YOU PROMISE TO SHOOT ME?
ZZ-ZZZ
OOF!
UMF!
struggle
COME ON - PULL YOUR FINGER OUT YOU DAFT OLD COW!

THERE - NOW CLEAR OFF BEFORE I SET THE BOBBIES ONTO YOU.

EEH. WHY DON'T THEY PUT THE BUS STOPS WHERE THEY'RE NEEDED? US OLD FOLK ALWAYS HAVE TO WALK MILES AND I'M NOT AS YOUNG AS I WAS YOU KNOW. AND NOBODY EVER BOTHERS TO LEND A HAND. EEH.

TIDDLES! TIDDLES! COME AND SEE WHAT MUMMY'S GOT FOR YOU! IT'S TEA TIME!

WHERE IS THE LITTLE SCALLYWAG? TIDDLES! TIDDLES! TIDDLES! TIDDLES!

WHERE ARE YOU HIDING?
COME TO MUMMY NOW TIDDLES! TIME FOR YOUR TEA! TIDDLES!!

PERHAPS HE'S IN HERE - TID-TID-TID-TID-TID! TID-TID-TID-TID-TID!

TIDDLES! TEATIME!

EEH - IT'S OUR SIDNEY'S CAR...

WE'LL MEET AGAIN... DON'T KNOW WHERE... DO
OH ADA...
OH SIDNEY...
THAT BRINGS BACK A FEW MEMORIES...

EEH - I THINK I'LL JUST POP INTO TOWN AND GET SOME CAT FOOD FOR TIDDLES.

SO...
EEH - THIS IS JUST LIKE DRIVING TRACTORS LIKE I DID WHEN I WAS A LAND GIRL IN THE WAR.
CRUNCH!
GRIND!
WWAAAAAAAA!
MIND YOU...

THE ROADS WERE MUCH WIDER IN THE OLDEN DAYS.
WHINE!
CLANG!
WHAT THE...?
JESUS!
AAAAAAAA

Bargain st
BUY 20 TINS OF CAT FOOD SECONDS & GET ONE FREE
CAT FOOD SPECIAL OFFERS ON BULK BUYS!
PUT PUT PUT PUT PUT

SHORTLY...
FIRE
NER! NER!
GRIND!
SMECK!
AAAAAAAAAA

SOME HOURS LATER...
HERE WE ARE - HOME AT LAST!
CRUNCH!
K-CLUNK!
AAAAAA
AAAAA
TIDDLES!! TEA-TIME!!
SPLAT!

WOOOO- WOOOO! TID-TID-TID-TID! TIDDLES!! TID-TID-TID-TID-TIDDLES!!!...
CAT FOOD
COME TO MUMMY!

# BUSTER GONAD & HIS UNFEASIBLY LARGE TESTICLES

DURING AN ELECTRICAL STORM BUSTER GONAD WAS STRUCK IN THE TESTICLES BY A METEORITE WHICH EMITTED STRANGE COSMIC RAYS.... ...: HIS TESTICLES GREW TO TITANIC PROPORTIONS AND AS HE SOON FOUND OUT, WITH GONADS AS BIG AS SOME--THING QUITE LARGE, ADVENTURE WAS NEVER VERY FAR AWAY, ETC.

SID THE SEXIST
TITS OOT! FOR THE LADS

IN THE STREET...
HOW LADS, CHECK OOT THE BAPS ON THAT WENCH!
BOING! FLUBBLE!
PHWOOAAR! PAIR O' BREESTS LIKE TWO PUPPIES FIGHTING IN A BAG, EH!?

OH AYE! ONE OF 'ER NIPS HAS POPPED OOT AN' AAL!
TOTTIESCOPE

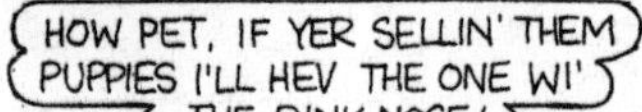
HOW PET, IF YER SELLIN' THEM PUPPIES I'LL HEV THE ONE WI' THE PINK NOSE!

WHAT?

OH VERY FUNNY, I'M SURE... HELLO DARLING, BEEN WAITING LONG?
JUST ARRIVED, SO, WHERE SHALL WE EAT?

HUNGRY, EH PET? D'YU LIKE CHICKEN?... SUCK ME COCK - IT'S FOWL!
WE COULD GO TO THAT NEW ITALIAN PLACE.

YER HEVVIN' NAE LUCK ON THE PULL EH, SID? Y'NEED SUMMIK TU IMPRESS THEM WITH, LIKE A FLASH MURTA O' SUMMIK.
AYE, THAT'S NORRA BAD IDEA THAT, BAZ.

NEXT DAY...
SUR YUV GOT YERSEL' A MURTA AALREADY?
AYE, A WENT DOON THE AUCTIONS THIS MORNIN' IT WAS A BARGAIN, MAN.

IT'S A SMART CAR, SEVENTY-SIX ON THE 'P.' TWO HUNDRED POOND, WI' TWO MONTHS TICKET AN' THREE WEEKS TAX.
AYE, IT'S AAL REET, LIKE.
IT MIGHT NEED SOME ATTENTION.
HMMM.

SUR, YU'LL BE OFF DOON THE COAST THE NEET THEN, EH SIDNEY?
WELL, A WOULD LIKE,... BUT, ERM, WELL...
BUT WHAT SID? YUR MURTA'S NOT CREAM-CRACKAD AALREADY IS IT?

WELL, NOT EXACTLY, IT'S JUST... WELL... THAT A CANNAT DRIVE.
YE WHAT?

A HAVE GOT SOME LESSONS BOOKED.
SID MAN, YORRABOOT NINEPENCE SHORT OF A SHILLIN'!
OH, 'EEZ NORRA FULL QUID LIKE.

A BIT LATER...
MR. SMUTT I PRESUME? I'M FROM THE MOTORING SCHOOL, I'M YOUR INSTRUCTOR.
BUT HAD ON..... YORRA WOMAN!

AN EXCELLENT OBSERVATION. NOW, YOU'RE PAYING FOR MY TIME SO I SUGGEST WE START THE LESSON STRAIGHT AWAY.

FIRST TIME I'VE EVER HAD TU PAY FOR A WOMAN, HEH! HEH! IT'S USUALLY ME WHAT TEACHES THE LASSES, IF Y'KNAA WORRA MEAN!

MIND, I LIKE YER NECKLACE PET, A COULD JUST FANCY SUMMIK AROOND ME NECK - YOUR LEGS! HEH! HEH! HEH!
VERY CLEVER ... YOUR FLY IS UNDONE.
AYE, THE CAGE IS OPEN, BUT THE BEAST IS ASLEEP.

UGH!
KRACK!!

LATER...
WELL... ERM, SHE COULDN'T KEEP 'ER HANDS OFF US MAN, THAT'S HOW SHE CRASHED THE CAR LIKE, AN' THAT'S HOW I GOT KNACKED!
PAH! HEY, WOMEN DRIVERS EH?!

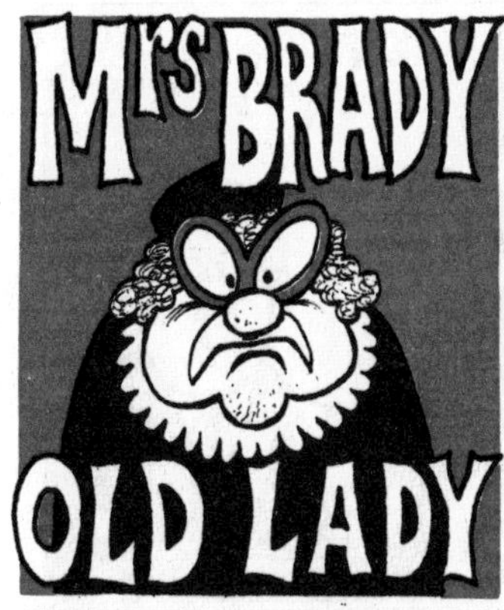

Mrs BRADY
OLD LADY

Newsagent

A TIN OF POWDERED EGG AND A COPY OF PICTURE POST. HERE'S ME RATION BOOK.
SORRY MRS. BRADY. 'PICTURE POST' CEASED PUBLICATION SOME 40 YEARS AGO.

WELL COULD YOU SLIP ME AN EXTRA COUPLE OF SAUSAGES THEN?
PRACTICAL FRETWORK
LOOK. THIS ISN'T A BUTCHERS AND RATIONING FINISHED IN THE EARLY 50'S. IT'S NOW 1988.

EEH. DOESN'T TIME FLY. IT ONLY SEEMS LIKE FIVE MINUTES SINCE I MARRIED OUR SIDNEY.

MIND YOU, I'VE NEVER BEEN WITH ANOTHER MAN. EEH. SIDNEY, GOD BLESS YOU. WHY DID YOU EVER HAVE TO LEAVE ME?
I'M EIGHTY-SEVEN AND I'VE STILL GOT ALL ME OWN TEETH.

EEH. THIS WAS ALL TREES WHEN I WAS A GIRL.
I'LL JUST POP IN HERE FOR ME RADIO TIMES.
TRAVEL AGENTS

HERE'S ME SIXPENCE
BUT THESE ARE FREE, MADAM.
SUNNYHOLS
WELL SIXPENCE IS ALL YOU'RE GETTING, YOU CHEEKY YOUNG DEVIL.

EEH. THEY'VE GOT THAT LOVELY MAN BOB MONKHOUSE ON THE COVER AGAIN.
BUS STOP
SUNNYHOLS

BACK HOME...
I WISH I'D BOUGHT ME RADIO TIMES, SO I COULD SEE WHAT'S ON TELLYVISION.
SUNNYHOLS
EEEH. ME PHOTO ALBUM. I MUST HAVE LOST THAT IN 1922 WHEN KING GEORGE WAS QUEEN.
SUNNYHOLS

OOH - THERE'S OUR ELSIE AND BERT. I REMEMBER THAT WAS TAKEN BEFORE SHE DIED.
AND THERE'S OUR SIDNEY. I NEVER LIKED HIM VERY MUCH. HIS EYES WERE TOO CLOSE TOGETHER.
YACHTING BREAKS
BOOKING FORM
I DON'T KNOW WHY I MARRIED HIM IN THE FIRST PLACE.

THEY NEVER COME TO SEE ME! NEVER! NONE OF 'EM! I COULD BE DEAD FOR ALL THEY KNOW. DEAD AND BURIED!
THEY DON'T EVEN PHONE. I CAN'T PHONE THEM COS I'M A PENSIONER AND IT'S TOO EXPENSIVE.


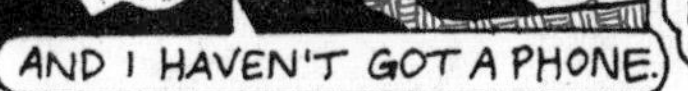

AND I HAVEN'T GOT A PHONE.

DING DONG
EEH! KIDS RINGING ME BELL AND RUNNING OFF. IF I'D HAVE DONE THAT WHEN I WAS A BOY I'D HAVE BEEN HORSEWHIPPED TO WITHIN AN INCH OF ME LIFE - AND I'D HAVE BEEN GRATEFUL FOR IT. WE WERE TAUGHT RESPECT IN THEM DAYS! I'LL SHOW 'EM.

HELLO ADA! IT'S US! ELSIE AND BERT! WE'VE COME TO SEE YOU!

EEH. YOU CAN'T GET A MINUTE'S PEACE WITHOUT FOLK TRAIPSING IN WITH THEIR KIDS. I SUPPOSE YOU'LL NOT BE HAPPY UNTIL YOU'VE HAD A CUP OF TEA OUT OF ME.

Norbert Colon
"He's Tight as a Gnat's Chuff"
XMAS TREE SHOP

Ting!
PUSH
£14
LOOK AT THIS! I BOUGHT THIS TREE AND ALL THE NEEDLES HAVE FALLEN OFF. I WANT MY MONEY BACK.

YOU DIDN'T BUY IT, COLON. I GAVE IT TO YOU EIGHT YEARS AGO, ON BOXING DAY, REMEMBER?

M-M-MERRY CH-CHRISMUSS P-PAL... HIC... OOOGH...

TCHOH! TCHOH! BLEEDING MARVELLOUS.
BLOOOAARGH!
HURK!

EEH! LOOK AT THAT! THERE MUST BE A GOOD HALF POUND OF DICED CARROT IN HERE.

WELL WASTE NOT WANT NOT, THAT'S WHAT I SAY. AND CARROTS IS A GOOD THREE SHILLINGS A POUND THESE DAYS YOU KNOW.
SCOOP
SCOOP

WELL THERE'S ME TWO VEG - I'D BEST GO AND GET SOME MEAT!

HAVE YOU GOT ANY FREE TURKEYS?
NO.
SO HOW MUCH ARE THEY THEN?

WELL THIS ONE'S FIFTEEN POUNDS.
SWOON!
MR. COLON - ARE YOU ALRIGHT?
SMACK!

PERHAPS YOU'D BE INTERESTED IN SOMETHING SMALLER.
HOW ABOUT THIS FOR TEN POUNDS?

TWO HOURS LATER...
WHAT ABOUT THIS? IT'S ONLY GOT ONE LEG AND IT DIED OF A RARE DISEASE. YOU CAN HAVE IT FOR NOTHING.
GO ON THEN - AS LONG AS YOU THROW IN A FEW SAUSAGES WITH IT.

GAH!
BOOT
BLOODY BUTCHERS! IT'S A LICENCE TO PRINT MONEY.
AND IT'S NOT AS IF I COULDN'T CATCH MY OWN CHRISTMAS DINNER.

THERE'S A NICE FAT ROBIN.
IT'LL LAST ME WEEKS, THAT WILL.

SO...
HO HO
CREAK
CREAK

WAAAH!
CRUNCH!

IN THE INTENSIVE CARE UNIT...
YOU'VE BROKEN YOUR SPINE, ALL YOUR LIMBS, AND SUFFERED CRITICAL INTERNAL INJURIES. YOU'LL NOT BE GOING HOME FOR AT LEAST 6 MONTHS.
HA!
THAT'LL DO ME! FREE BOARD AND LODGINGS!

BUT HANG ON - IT SAYS HERE THAT YOU HAVEN'T PAID ANY NATIONAL INSURANCE CONTRIBUTIONS SINCE 1949. OH DEAR... I'M AFRAID WE'RE GOING TO HAVE TO SWITCH OFF YOUR LIFE SUPPORT MACHINE, MR. COLON.
HRUMPH!

Johnny
HONK!
FartPants
A PUMP, A SMILE AND AN AWFUL PONG.

SO JOHNNY, TELL ME AGAIN, WHAT WAS YOUR NEW YEAR RESOLUTION?
TO GIVE UP PUMPING FOR ONCE AND FOR ALL - I'LL NEVER CHUFF AGAIN!

NOW, WE'RE GOING TO SEE AUNTIE GLADIOLI TODAY AND IN ORDER TO KEEP YOU ON YOUR BEST BEHAVIOUR I'LL BE BRINGING ALONG A COAL-BOARD SURPLUS FIREDAMP CANARY AND A GAS-CROMATOGRAPH MASS-SPECTROMETER TO SEEK OUT EVEN THE TINIEST TRACES OF TRUMP-TOMFOOLERY!

THE MOMENT I DETECT ANY MARSH-GAS MANIFESTATIONS I'LL BE STOPPING YOUR POCKET MONEY!
YIKE!

OOH-ER! I'D BETTER TRY ABSOLOUTELY-COMPLETELY MY HARDEST NOT TO POP-A-CHUFF FOR A WHOLE DAY!

SO...
YOU DON'T NEED THE TOILET DO YOU JOHNNY? IT'S A LONG WAY TO AUNTIE GLAD'S HOUSE IN THE COUNTRYSIDE.
NOT VERY FRESH FISH
SPECIALIST IN THREE WEEK OLD MACKERAL
NO MUM, I'M OKAY.

SQGGRQEECH!
FISHMONGER'S WELLIES SCUFF TOGETHER
?
YAROO!

HONESTLY JOHNNY! WE'VE NOT SET OFF AND ALREADY YOU'RE PERFORMING YOUR ANEMOPHILOUS AEROBOTICS!
BUT FATHER, I PROTEST! I HAVEN'T STEPPED ON A FROG ONCE TODAY-HONEST.

RUBBISH! LOOK, THE CANARY'S DEAD ALREADY. YOU'LL BE GETTING NO POCKET MONEY FOR A MONTH!
BUT... BUT... BUT... ?!?

A BIT LATER...
OH WELL, LOOKS LIKE WE MADE TOO MUCH CHEESE AGAIN TODAY, LET'S JUST DUMP IT HERE NEXT TO YESTERDAYS.
CHEESE FACTORY
OKAY, I'LL SOUND THE HOOTER FOR THE NEXT SHIFT.

FWOOHUUUFFF!
SMELL OF ROTTEN CHEESE WAFTS THROUGH CAR WINDOWS
RIGHT! NO POCKET MONEY UNTIL MARCH!

BUT DAD! IT WASN'T ME!
IT'S TOO LATE JOHNNY, YOU'RE THE BOY WHO PUMPED WOLF!

FURTHER ON...
AAH! AT LAST A PLACE WHERE I FEEL I CAN RELEASE MY ARTISTIC BENT! I CAN PRACTICE PROLONGED SINGLE NOTES ON MY BASS TROMBONE ALL DAY LONG!

BVRVAUAUAUPHQH!
JOHNNY!
ABANDONED SULPHUR FACTORY AND EGG WAREHOUSE

AT A NEARBY WEATHER CENTRE...
I SAY! LOOK! THE WIND HAS SUDDENLY CHANGED DIRECTION AND IS BLOWING ACROSS THE ABANDONED SULPHUR FACTORY AND EGG WAREHOUSE TOWARDS THE MAIN ROAD!
ABSOLOUTELY FASCINATING.

PRESENTLY...
IT'S NO USE LYING JOHNNY, THE MACHINE REGISTERS TRACES OF SODIUM-CHUFFATE AND DI-NITROGEN FARTOXIDE!
BUT...
APRIL!

LATER, AT AUNTIE GLADIOLI'S...
ENJOYING YOUR TEA EVERYONE? I'LL JUST FEED THE CAT... COME ALONG TRUFFLES.

PzKGSQREEUU!
JOHNNY-MAY!
AWW... DAD!
RUBBER GLOVE ON KITCHEN LINO

JFSZQFUEEECGGRRHH!
must remember to oil this fridge door.
JUNE!

OFFAL
Supreme
ECONOMY CAT FOOD
WE MUST FINISH THIS TIN TRUFFLES, IT'S SIX WEEKS SINCE WE OPENED IT NOW.


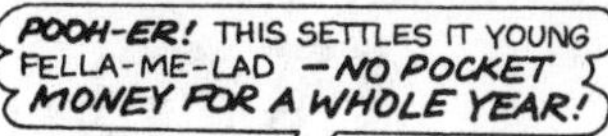

POOH-ER! THIS SETTLES IT YOUNG FELLA-ME-LAD -NO POCKET MONEY FOR A WHOLE YEAR!

OH NO... NO... OH NO... NO... NO...

...NO ...NO ...OH ... ... YULOOP! I'VE FALLEN ASLEEP IN THE BATH, IT WAS ALL A DREAM, MY MONEY'S SAFE!
OH YINKS!
RUMBLE! FLUBBLE! GRUNDGLEG! RBLOGGLRLUPPLE!

RHFUBBO-BULLOOSCH!

LATER...
WELL JOHNNY THAT DEPTH CHARGE YOU DROPPED IN THE BATH (WHICH BLEW 40 GALLONS OF WATER ONTO THE FLOOR) HAS CRACKED THE CAST IRON BATH AND FLOODED THE KITCHEN. TO PAY FOR THE DAMAGE YOU'LL GET NO POCKET-MONEY FOR A WHOLE YEAR!
BLUE RUIN!

BIFFA
MERRY
XMAS
BACON

CHRISTMAS EVE...
HOY, BIFFA! COME AN' LOOK AT THIS

WHAT THE FUCK IS IT MAN, FATHA?

ITS A DOOR SON!
WHAM!
OOO-ERK!!

AND GUESS WHAT THIS IS
HEH HEH!

IT'S A FUCKIN' IRON!
CLANG!
YAADOOGFF!!

AH, COME ON SON. YORRA GOOD LAD. YA MUTHA AN ME WAS ONLY KIDDIN'.
I'LL TELL Y'WHAT. WHY DIVVUN Y'GAN OOT AN GERRUS A NICE BIG CHRISMUSS TREE?!

ALREET THEN, Y'FUCKIN BASTAADS
AN BIFFA...

DIVVUN FORGET YA SHOVEL!
BLAT!!

SHORTLY...
AH! THAT'LL DEE!

I SAY! JUST WHAT THE HELL DO YOU THINK YOU'RE DOING?!

PISS OFF!

NOW THAT'S FAR ENOUGH!

NOW JUST YOU LISTEN TO ME YOUNG MAN...
COME BACK HERE THIS MINUTE, I TELL YOU!

LATER...
AYE SON. THAT'S A CANNY TREE!
IT LOOKS FUCKIN' CHAMPION!

DING DONG!
WHO THE FUCK'S THAT?

EXCUSE ME, BUT YOUR SON HAS JUST STOLEN MY PRIZE MAGNOLIA TREE!

BIFFA. DID YOU PINCH THIS MAN'S TREE?
AYE FATHA!
THERE YOU ARE. I TOLD YOU SO...

SMACK!
OOOF!

YORRA GOOD LAD, BIFFA!

LATER...
FATHA. I CANN'T WAIT TILL THE 'MORRA. GIZ ME FUCKIN' PRESENT NOO!
IT'S UNDER THE TREE

HEY! I WONDER WORRIT IS. IT WEIGHS A TON!

OOOF!!

HAPPY CHRISTMAS BIFFA!
Y'FRIGGIN' BASTARD!

HOY BIFFA. LOOK WHO'S HERE. IT'S YA GRANNY. SHE'S GOT Y'A PRESENT
IT'S NOTHING SPECIAL...
BUT I DO HOPE YOU LIKE IT!

I KNITTED IT MYSELF
I'M NOT WEARIN' THAT! IT LOOKS SOFT!
DIVVUN BE UNGRATEFUL BIFFA. PUT THE FUCKA ON!

OOH, DOESN'T HE LOOK LOVELY
YOU LOOK LIKE A FUCKIN' PUFF T'ME

I SAID YOU LOOK LIKE A PUFF. WHAT Y'GANNA DEE ABOORIT?
OH DEAR...
I HOPE I HAVEN'T CAUSED ANY TROUBLE

SMACK!
OOOF!
AAAGH!!
WHAM!

STOBBIT- THE PAIR O'YERS! I DIVVUN WANT NEY FIGHTIN' IN WOR HOOS THIS CHRISMUSS

Y'BASTARDS!!
CRACK!

DING DONG!
WHO THE FUCK IS IT NOO?

THAT'S HIM! THAT'S THE MAN WHO ASSAULTED ME OFFICER

BLAT!
GNMMPFF!!

RIGHT SON. YOU'RE NICKED!

IS THERE A PROBLEM HERE, FATHA?
AYE, WOMAN...
THIS COPPA HERE CALLED Y'A WHOO-ER!!

THUD!

CHRISTMAS MORNING...
I'VE BROUGHT YOU ALL YOUR CHRISTMAS DINNER... BREAD AND WATER! ARF ARF!! HAPPY CHRISTMAS EVERYONE!
HADAWAY AND SHITE!
CD. GPD. S.T.

SID THE SEXIST
TITSOOT!!

NEW YEAR'S EVE...
HOW LADS, THEZ GORRA BE SUMMIK BERRA T'DEE THAN WAALK THE STREET.
HEY SID, I THOWT YE WUZ GANNA FIX US AAL UP WITH A CLASS LEG-AWA!

HOWAY, LEAVE UZ ALURN LADS, YUZ AAL KNAA THERE WUZ NOWT BEYTIN' IN THAT BAR... ANYWAYS-LOOK-A PARTY!
AYE! THIS'LL DEE LADS!

SO...
YES, CAN I HELP YOU?
erm... WELL WE DIVVEN'T WANNA COME IN LIKE...
oh no... norruss, nowt like that.
naah..nah.
naah...
... AYE... WERE JUST LOOKIN' FOR SOMEONE... erm... FRED... AYE, AYE FRED... AYE.

FRED - OF COURSE - HE JUST LEFT A MOMENT AGO, RUN ALONG AND YOU MIGHT CATCH HIM.
SLAM!

MOMENTS LATER...

LERRUZ IN Y'BASTADS!
REYT... LET'S FIND AAL THE PLONK!

DOWNSTAIRS...
MIND IT'S A CLASS DO THIS EH? BAGS O' POSH FLUFF AROOND SID.
AYE BAZ, AN IT'S NEW YAIR - W'CAN SNOG THEM AAL!

HOWAY PET, GIZ A NEW-YAIR KISS!
IT'S NOT MIDNIGHT YET!
I DIVVEN'T WANT NONE OF YER POOFY KISSES MIND, A WANT A FRENCH ONE, WI' TONGUES N' THAT.
DON'T BE SO DISGUSTING!

LISTEN PET, A KNAA WORRA LIKE ... AN' A LIKE WORRA SEE.
WHY DON'T YOU LEAVE ME ALONE YOU FUCKING CORNY TWAT ?!

LISTEN PET, D'Y'KNAA THE ESSENTIAL DIFFERENCE BETWEEN SEX AND CONVERSATION?
JESUS! THAT'S ANCIENT... 'COME UPSTAIRS - I WANT TO TALK TO YOU'

...WELL COME UPSTAIRS - A WANNA TAALK TU... YU... FUCK!
NOT YOUR DAY, EH SID?! HEH! HEH! HEH!

HE'S A CHEEKY GET EH? MIND THAT'S A SMART PIECE WORREEZ PULLED THO' BUT!
SHE LOOKS LIKE SOMEONE'S BEEN CHOPPIN' FIREWOOD ON 'ER FACE!

ROUGH AS A BADGER'S ARSE!
YER AWNLY JEALOUS SID!
I'M NOT, REYT!
OH AYE, I SUPPOSE YE'VE HED 'ER?
AYE! A FUCKIN' HEV... SHE'S GOT PUBES LIKE 13AMP FUSE WIRE!
Shiloe & Co. '88

FERGERRIT MAN SID - JUST HEV A BIT LAUGH AN' CARRY-ON!
FACE LIKE A SACK O' CHISELS!

11·45...
LISTEN, WE WOULDN'T OBJECT TO YOUR UNINVITED PRESENCE HERE IF YOUR FRIEND WASN'T BEING SO OFFENSIVE. COULD YOU POSSIBLY DO SOMETHING ABOUT HIM?
AYE MATE, AAL REET.
D'Y'KAA WORRA WOMAN SEZ AFTA 17 ORGASMS? - "THANKS SID."

whisper... whisper
HOW PET, WILL YU KISS US UNDER THE MISTLETOE?
HUH!
WIGGLE WIGGLE
whisper... plot, plan, whisper...

HOW SID, GREAT IDEA! YER GANNA BE THE FORST-FOOT!
HERE'S A GOOD 'N - WHAT WINKS AND MAKES LOVE LIKE A TIGER?
OH GOD, DO TELL ME!

HOW MAN!
Jesus.
WINK!
COAL
LISTEN SID, COP A HAD O' THIS AN' GERROOT THE DOOR - WHEN IT GANS 12 RING THE BELL AN' YE CAN COME IN AN' SNOG THE LASSES.

3 am...
mmf... GROAN... SLURP!
OOH LA LA!
KNOCK KNOCK!
HOWAY LADS!... A JOKES A JOKE.... HOWAY... LERRUS IN... Aaaah HOWAY... LERRUS IN.... Y'BASTADS!!

DURING AN ELECTRICAL STORM BUSTER GONAD WAS STRUCK IN THE TESTICLES BY A METEORITE WHICH EMITTED STRANGE COSMIC RAYS.... ...HIS TESTICLES GREW TO TITANIC PROPORTIONS AND AS HE SOON FOUND OUT, WITH GONADS AS BIG AS SOME--THING QUITE LARGE, ADVENTURE WAS NEVER VERY FAR AWAY, ETC.

# Postman Plod

## *The Miserable Bastard*

LATER...
HE'S GOT A PARCEL, MUM. IS IT FOR ME? OOOH! MUM, IT'S FOR ME, LOOK, IT'S FOR ME!!

I WONDER WHAT IT IS, MUM!
I DON'T KNOW, BILLY. YOU'LL HAVE TO WAIT UNTIL CHRISTMAS DAY. IT'LL BE A NICE SURPRISE FOR YOU!

DON'T GET TOO EXCITED, KID!
IT'S ONLY A CHEAP PLASTIC RACING CAR! HONG KONG! IT'LL BE KNACKERED BY BOXING DAY!

SHORTLY...
THERE HE IS! THERE HE IS!

PLEASE, MR. POSTMAN. CAN YOU DELIVER THIS LETTER TO SANTA CLAUS? HE LIVES IN GREENLAND.

GREENLAND, EH? THAT'S BLOODY MILES AWAY! HOW MUCH MONEY HAVE YOU GOT?

COME ON, COME ON! ALL OF IT!

ONE POUND TWENTY NINE? IS THAT ALL.....
....OH, ALLRIGHT! I'LL MAKE SURE IT GETS TO HIM!

HEH HEH!
RIGHT! NOW TO PICK UP SOME PROPER TIPS!

EVENTUALLY...
FOUR POUND FIFTY! I ASK YOU! FOUR POUND FUCKIN' FIFTY! CAH!
SEASON OF GOOD WILL MY ARSE!

OY! HOW MUCH DID YOU GET THEN?
EH?
CHRISTMAS TIPS, YOU DAFT BASTARD! HOW MUCH?

OH, THAT! ABOUT FIFTY QUID ALTOGETHER

COME ON, THEN! HAND IT OVER!
WHY?

BECAUSE IT'S MINE, THAT'S WHY. IT'S THE RULE IN THIS OFFICE!!

REALLY? HOW FASCINATING! AND JUST WHAT RULE, PRAY TELL, IS THAT?

THIS ONE!
SMACK!

THAT NIGHT...
M-M-MERRY CHR... HIC! M-M-HIC!... M-MERRY HIC! M-HIC! AH FUCK IT!

SPOILT BASTARD
ONE DAY...
MOTHER, I WANT SOME SHOES AND I WANT THEM NOW!

BUT I ONLY BOUGHT YOU THOSE YESTERDAY. YOU DON'T NEED ANY MORE MY ANGEL!
SHOES SHOES SHOES SHOES SHOES SHOES

INSIDE...
SHOW ME THE MOST EXPENSIVE SHOES IN THE SHOP!

WELL, THAT'S THESE HAND STITCHED ITALIAN BROGUES BUT WE ONLY HAVE THEM TO FIT MEN!
I WANT THEM!

BUT THEY DON'T HAVE THEM IN YOUR SIZE, TIMOTHY MY DARLING!
I WANT THEM!

THEY'RE FAR TOO BIG FOR YOU. LISTEN TO MUMMY!
WANT THEM!

AND THEY'RE A LITTLE BIT EXPENSIVE

GOODNESS!
OH, DEAR ME!
WAAAH!

AND...
SNIFF!
SHO

BACK HOME
NOT TOO TIGHT! OR PERHAPS YOU WANT TO RUIN MY FEET!! BLINKING FLIP, MOTHER, DO YOU EVER GET ANYTHING RIGHT?

LOOK, MOTHER, THEY'RE TOO BIG. I LOOK STUPID! I HOPE YOU'RE PLEASED WITH YOURSELF!
BUT YOU WANTED THEM, DEAR!

I DID NOT WANT THEM! YOU MADE ME HAVE THEM AND NOW EVERYONE WILL LAUGH AT ME!! I ABSOLUTELY HATE YOU, MOTHER!
THERE THERE
BOO! HOO!

SNIFF! I'M SORRY, TREASURE. SOB! I'LL COOK YOU YOUR FAVOURITE TEA TO MAKE UP.
YES YOU WILL!!

HERE WE ARE MY LITTLE PRINCE! EAT THESE EXPENSIVE CONTINENTAL TRUFFLES WHILST I MAKE IT!
HA!

SHORTLY...
HERE WE ARE MY LITTLE POPPET! I'VE CUT UP YOUR FISH FINGERS FOR YOU! DO YOU WANT TOMATO SAUCE ON IT?
OF COURSE I DO!

OOPS!
FLIP!

AAAARGH! YOU'VE PUT IT ON MY PEAS, YOU STUPID, STUPID OLD HAG! YOU'VE RUINED IT NOW!
I CAN'T EAT IT! I CAN'T EAT IT AND I WON'T EAT IT!

OH FORGIVE ME MY LITTLE SOLDIER!
DO IT AGAIN!!

SHORTLY...
HERE WE ARE, DEAR!
I'VE CHECKED YOUR FISH-FINGERS FOR GREY BITS!

BUT...
AAAAARGH!
CHOKE!
GAG!

TIMMY!
BLOARGH!

A BONE! THERE WAS A BONE IN MY FISHFINGER! MY GOD! YOU'RE TRYING TO KILL ME YOU WITCH!

YOU KEEP AWAY FROM ME! HELP! POLICE!
NO, TIMMY! COME BACK!

I'LL KILL MYSELF AND SAVE YOU THE BOTHER, SHALL I?
DON'T BE SILLY!

I'M GOING TO HOLD MY BREATH UNTIL I DIE!

NO, TIMOTHY, DON'T! HERE'S SOME SWEETS

LATER...
HELLO. IS THAT THE N.S.P.C.C.?
MY PARENTS ARE TRYING TO KILL ME!

HELLO.
I'M A SOCIAL WORKER AND I'M AFRAID I HAVE TO TAKE YOUR SON TO A CHILDRENS HOME!

AT THE FULCHESTER HOME FOR PROBLEM CHILDREN...
OOF! HA! THIS'LL TEACH HER! OOF! I BET SHE'S SORRY NOW!!
G.R.D. S.T. S.D. 88

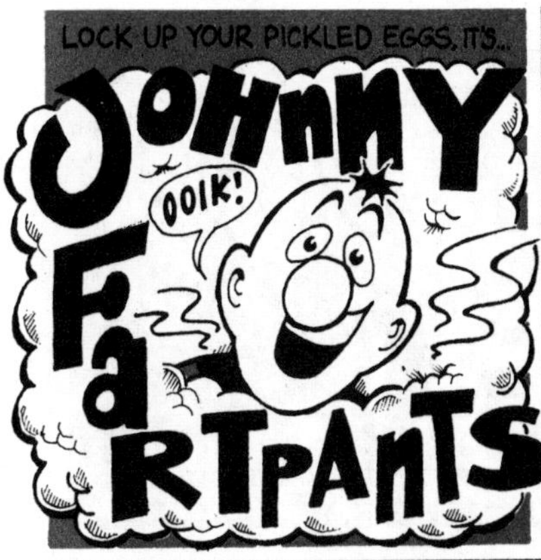
LOCK UP YOUR PICKLED EGGS, IT'S..
JOHNNY FARTPANTS
OOIK!

HALLO READERS! I'M OFF TO BUY A COPY OF JOKE FUNNIES WITH MY LAST PENNIES...
BARK!

POOH-ER! THAT WAS A BEEFY-EGGO!
BIG DAIRY GOODS ENTRANCE
MILK STOREROOM FRESH AIR INTAKE

LATER...
I'M FROM THE BIG DAIRY, ALL OUR MILK HAS CURDLED AS A RESULT OF A TERRIBLE PUMP WHICH YOUR SON LET-OFF AS HE PASSED BY. I'M AFRAID YOU MUST PAY ME ONE HUNDRED POUNDS.
?!

WELL JOHNNY, AT 50P A WEEK, THAT'LL BE NO POCKET MONEY FOR YOU FOR THE NEXT FOUR YEARS!
!
CORKS!
TISH AND PISH!

A BIT LATER...
BAH! NO CASH FOR FOUR YEARS, WHAT A CALAMITY! ... BUT HOLD ON - WHAT'S THIS?
GRAND TALENT CONTEST AT THE TOWN HALL TONITE
PRIZE £100
PRESENTED BY THE LORD MAYOR

SO...
HELLO FOLKS! I'D LIKE TO DO SOME FARMYARD IMPRESSIONS FOR YOU... FIRST OF ALL - LISTEN! THE HINGES ON THE BARN DOOR NEEDA SPOT OF OIL...
JOHNNY FARTPANTS AND HIS TALKING TROUSERS

GKSQVPPROOUUEEEEEEEEBE
GNN!

CLAP! CLAP! HOORAY!
THANKYOU! THANKYOU! AND NOW WE GO DOWN TO THE DUCKPOND...

QUACK!
CLAP! CHEER! APPLAUD!

HARK! THE LITTLE PIGLETS ARE AT THE TROUGH!

OINK!
SHRIKE! SHRIKE!
GSQQNURRK! GSQQNURRK!
OINK!

AND FINALLY, IT'S A FROSTY MORNING AS THE FARMER TRIES TO START UP HIS TRACTOR...
K-CHUG K-CHUG FUWOON FULUF!
hfreeeee -eeeeee fwhree GU-JUGGU! etc.

HOORAY! HOORAY!
WELL SON, THERE'S NO DOUBT - YOU'RE THE OUTRIGHT WINNER. HERE'S £100 - NOW, HOW ABOUT AN ENCORE?

CERTAINLY, I'D LIKE TO SING A LITTLE SONG WHAT I'VE WRITTEN.

SO...
MY NAME IS JOHNNY FARTPANTS I REALLY LOVE TO PUMP, WHEN YOU HEAR ME BLOW ONE OFF IT'S SURE TO MAKE YOU JUMP,...

I LIVE ON CABBAGE WATER AND WEEK-OLD PICNIC EGGS, THEY DO JUST WHAT THEY OUGHTA SENDING RUMBLES THROUGH MY KEGS,...

THE SMELL IS QUITE APPALLING - IMPOSSIBLE TO MISS, AND IF YOU DON'T BELIEVE ME THEN SEW A BUTTON ON THIS!
CLANG!

PREDICTABLY...
I AM A STRUCTURAL ENGINEER, AND THE DAMAGE WHICH THAT CLIMACTIC FLUFF HAS DONE TO THE FOUNDATIONS OF THE BUILDING WILL COST £100 TO REPAIR!

I'LL HAVE THAT BACK YOUNG MAN!
!
BAH!

SID THE SEXIST
TITSOOT!

SATURDAY AFTERNOON...

LOOK LADS! IT'S SIDNEY! HE'S AALL DONE-UP LIKE A DOG'S DINNER!
AAH SHITE!
LOOKS MORE LIKE A PIG'S BREAKFAST!

SORRY TU HEAR ABOOT YER MAM, SID!
EH?!
YER NANA'S IN HOSPITAL IS SHE SIDNEY?
NAR MAN, HIS SISTER'S HAD A BAIRN MAN.

WHAT THE FRIG ARE YUZ AALL TAAKIN' ABOOT?!
HOWAY MAN SID, Y'CANNAT HAVE BOUGHT FLOWAZ FOR A LASS THO' BUT!

ARE YU CUMMIN' TU THE MATCH SID? DENTIST'S CLOSED THEN EH?
DENTIST?... OH AYE... ERM NAH... NOT REALLY.
WHAT'S THIS IN YER POCKET SID?

FUCK OFF! FUCK OFF! FUCK OFF Y'BASTAD! FUCK OFF! HOWAY HOWAY FUCK OFF Y'BASTAD!
"YOUR COMPUTER DATE DENISE WILL MEET YOU AT THE MONUMENT METRO STATION AT TWO O'CLOCK ON SATURDAY - DON'T BE LATE."

COMPUTER DATE SID? A BLOKE WITH YOUR PULLIN' POWER?!
NAR, NOT ME, NAR, THAT'S ME FATHA'S, HE'S HAD ME SUIT ON MAN - LEFT IT IN THE POCKET!

SUR 'EEZ FINALLY TURNED UP THEN HAZ 'E SID?
ERM... WELL NOT EXACTLY...
BUT LADS! THIS CARD'S ADDRESSED TO MR. SIDNEY SMUTT!

HOWAY LADS, YE'LL MISS THE KICK-OFF, LEAVE US ALURN! A'M AWNLY DEEIN' THIS FORRABIT LAUGH'N' CARRY-ON! HEY MAN A'LL GERRA SHAG OOT OF IT AN'AALL!
DIVVEN'T WURRY ABOORR'US MAN SID, WE'LL HANG AROOND AN' HEV A BUTCHAZ AT THIS LASS!

HOWAY LADS, LEAVE US ALURN WILL YUZ!
FUCK ME SIDNEY! IS THIS YOUR LASS?
JEEZUZ SHIT!
CHRIST ALL-FUCKIN'-MIGHTY, IT CANNAT BE, SID!

GUMPH! HEH! HEH! AYE LADS, THIS'LL BE THE ONE ALRIGHT!
HEY SID, IF SHE'S GUNNA GAN OOT WI YE, SHE CANNAT HEV MUCH UPSTAIRS!
AYE... BUT WHAT A FUCKIN' STAIRCASE THOUGH!

HOW, YE MUST BE DENISE, IF YE LIKE FRUIT, SUCK ON ME COCK - IT'S A PEACH!

A BIT LATER...
IT'S A GOOD JOB THAT WUZ THE WRONG LASS, COZ SHE WUZ OBVIOUSLY A LESBIAN!
AYE, DOUBTLESS.
AYE, AYE.
AYE, SID.
EXCUSE ME, ARE YOU SIDNEY?...

... SIDNEY? FROM THE DATING AGENCY?
GUMPH!
WHAT!?
FUCK ME LADS! A YETI IN KNICKERS!

HEH! HEH! WELL, THEY ERM.. AALL LOOK THE SAME IN THE DARK, EH LADS?
AYE, AN' EVERY TIME SHE BENDS AWA IT WILL BE FUCKIN' DARK! WE'LL LOSE AN HOUR OF DAYLIGHT! HA! HA! HA!
!
HEY, YE'D HEV MORE FUN SHAGGIN' A SACK O' PEASE PUDDIN' HEH! HEH!
AN' YE WOULDN'T HEV TU TEK IT YEM AFTA! HO! HO!

SID MAN, A'VE SEEN THIS LASS DOON THE BEACH - THE RSPCA WERE TRYIN' TU GERRA BACK IN THE WATTA! HO! HO! HO!
HOW SID, IF YA GANNA SAY IT WI' FLOWERS Y'SHOULD OF BRUNG A FUCKIN' CACTUS!

NEVER MIND SID, WHEN YER ON THE JOB YE CAN JUST SLAP THE FAT AN' RIDE THE WAVES!
SHUT YA FUCKIN' MOOTH!
COME ON DENISE, NO SISTER OF MINE IS GOING OUT WITH THIS KIND OF ANIMAL!

WHAT?!!

YOU BASTARDS.
HO! HO!
HA! HA!
HA! HA! HA! HO! HO!

FELIX and his AMAZING underpants
CD GPD 89

FELIX IS LOOKING FOR A JOB...
AH! HERE'S A JOB FOR YOU. IT'S A GOVERNMENT TRAINING SCHEME VACANCY AT THE ZOO
JOB CENTRE
GREAT! I'VE ALWAYS WANTED TO WORK WITH ANIMALS

AT THE ZOO...
I'VE COME ABOUT THE JOB
HERE. YOU'LL NEED THIS

WE HAVE RATHER A PROBLEM WITH ELEPHANT DROPPINGS HERE AT THE ZOO. YOUR JOB IS TO SWEEP THEM ALL UP!

THREE HOURS LATER...
WELL, IT'S A LOT TIDIER, BUT WHAT I NEED NOW IS SOMEWHERE TO PUT IT ALL

THAT'S AMAZING FELIX! I'VE NEVER SEEN THE PLACE SO TIDY. NOT A SIGN OF EXCREMENT ANYWHERE! I DON'T KNOW HOW YOU DO IT

LATER...
BLOODY HELL. THESE EGGS SHOULD HAVE HATCHED BY NOW!

DON'T WORRY. I'LL CRAM THEM INTO MY UNDIES - THEY MAKE AN IDEAL INCUBATOR!
WHAT A BRILLIANT IDEA!

SOME TIME LATER...
CRACK!
AH! AT LAST
CRUNCH!
THEY'RE BEGINING TO HATCH

SNAP!!
YEEAGGH!
SNAP!
GNAW!
SNAP!
SNAP!
GNASH!!

AGGH! OUCH!! YEEEOW!!
SNAP!
SNAP!
SNAP!!

POOR FELIX. I FORGOT TO MENTION THOSE WERE CROCODILES EGGS!

EVEN LATER STILL...
WHAT'S THE MATTER WITH HIM MR ZOO KEEPER? HE LOOKS A BIT DEPRESSED
I'M AFRAID WE'VE RUN OUT OF SAND. AS A RESULT THE POOR OSTRICH HAS GOT NOWHERE TO BURY ITS HEAD

CHEER UP MISTER OSTRICH!
YOU CAN BURY YOUR HEAD IN MY UNDERPANTS!

WELL DONE FELIX! YOUR AMAZING UNDERPANTS HAVE SAVED THE DAY YET AGAIN!

PRESENTLY...
IT'S FEEDING TIME FELIX. CAN YOU HELP ME GET THIS UNUSUALLY LARGE SACK OF BUNS TO THE ELEPHANTS
EASY!
BUNS

I'LL SIMPLY TOSS A SUPPLY OF BUNS INTO MY OUTSTRETCHED UNDERWEAR...
LIKE SO...

THEN DISTRIBUTE THEM BY MEANS OF AN IMPROVISED UNDERPANT SLING!
WHOOSH!

OOPS! THE SOMEWHAT INACCURATE PERFORMANCE OF MY PANTS HAS PRODUCED A COMPLETELY RANDOM DISTRIBUTION OF BUNS

YOU BLUNDERING OAF! A STRAY BUN HAS HIT AND KILLED SKIPPER THE KANGAROO, LEAVING HER YOUNG JOEY MOTHERLESS!
CRUMBS!

THERE'S ONLY ONE THING FOR IT! YOU'LL HAVE TO REAR THE YOUNG JOEY YOURSELF, USING YOUR UNDERPANTS AS A FORM OF SURROGATE POUCH!

INCIDENTALLY, IN THE WILD A KANGAROO BABY REMAINS IN ITS MOTHER'S POUCH FOR 2 YEARS!
HO HO HO! I'LL SEE YOU IN 2 YEAR'S TIME, FELIX!!

TUBBY JOHNSON

He's as fat as I don't know what!

ONE DAY
GIVE ME A LIFT TO THE CAKE SHOP, POP! I HAVEN'T EATEN FOR TEN MINUTES!
BLAH BLAH

NO, TUBBY! I'VE HAD TO SELL THE CAR TO PAY FOR ALL YOUR FOOD, YOU FAT BASTARD! IN FACT, SON, WE CAN'T AFFORD TO FEED YOU ANYMORE! YOU'LL HAVE TO GO OUT AND GET A JOB
HUNH?

HERE'S THE PAPER! THERE'S BOUND TO BE A JOB IN THERE FOR YOU!

BAH! ALL THESE JOBS ARE FOR SKINNIES!
SITUATIONS VACANT
SKINNY
THIN
ARE YOU THIN?
THIN
SKINNY
LEAN PER SON
NOT FAT

FULCHESTER BUN FACTORY NEEDS A PERSON TO TEST THEIR BUNS APPLY IN PERSON. THIS POST IS OPEN TO BOTH FATTIES AND NORMAL PEOPLE
HEY, WOW! THAT'S FOR ME!

LATER...
I'M OFF TO GET THAT JOB, READERS.

HEY, TUBBY!
TOFFEE FACTORY

WE'VE MADE FAR TOO MUCH TOFFEE TODAY AND ALL THE DUSTBINS ARE FULL. IF YOU COME IN AND EAT IT FOR US, WE'LL GIVE YOU A TENNER!!
NO, I'M SORRY, I CAN'T! I'M IN A HURRY

CRUMBS!

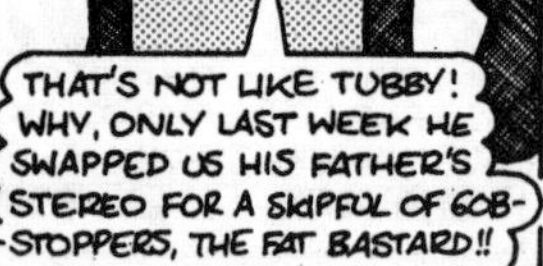
THAT'S NOT LIKE TUBBY! WHY, ONLY LAST WEEK HE SWAPPED US HIS FATHER'S STEREO FOR A SKIPFUL OF GOB-STOPPERS, THE FAT BASTARD!!

GOD, I HOPE I GET THAT JOB! I'M STARVING! LOOK, I MUST HAVE LOST A STONE ALREADY!!

FULCHESTER PORK PIES
TUBBY, TUBBY! THANK GOODNESS WE'VE FOUND YOU!

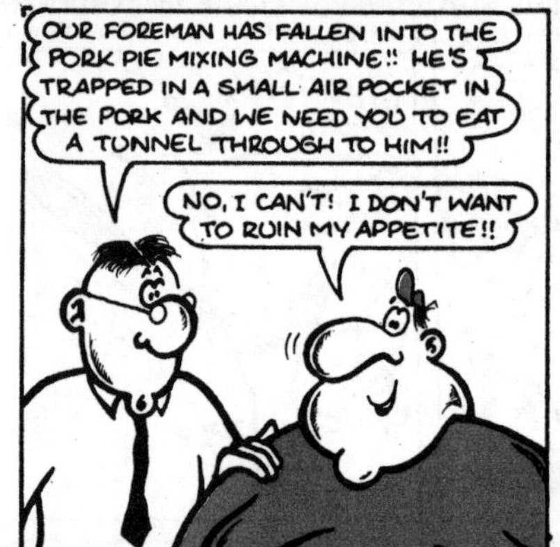
OUR FOREMAN HAS FALLEN INTO THE PORK PIE MIXING MACHINE!! HE'S TRAPPED IN A SMALL AIR POCKET IN THE PORK AND WE NEED YOU TO EAT A TUNNEL THROUGH TO HIM!!
NO, I CAN'T! I DON'T WANT TO RUIN MY APPETITE!!

WELL I NEVER!
WHAT AN UNUSUAL RESPONSE FROM THE FAT YOUNGSTER WHO ONLY THE OTHER DAY ATE THREE METRIC TONNES OF WASTE LARD!!

AT THE BUN FACTORY...
INTERVIEWS
KNOCK KNOCK

SHORTLY...
WELL, TUBBY! YOU'VE GOT THE JOB! WHEN CAN YOU START?
NOW!

WELL, YOU'LL TEST BUNS FOR TWELVE HOURS A DAY, SEVEN DAYS A WEEK. YOU'LL GET A POUND PER WEEK, FIVE MINUTES DINNER BREAK AND NO HOLIDAYS!
YES, YES, JUST TAKE ME TO THE BUNS!

JUST SIGN THIS TWENTY YEAR CONTRACT!
OKAY, OKAY. NOW CAN I START TESTING?

NOT SURPRISINGLY...
THIS IS WHERE YOU WILL TEST THE BUN-STYLE HAIRPIECES!
ARRRGH NO! NOT THOSE TYPE OF BUNS!

SO...
BUNS TESTED SO FAR
7431062½
BAH!!

TOMMY AND HIS MAGIC ARSE
HI READERS! I'M TOMMY THOMPSON!

AND THIS IS MY MAGIC ARSE!

BUT IT'S NOT MAGIC ALL THE TIME - ONLY WHEN I TALK IN RHYME!

OH NO! I'VE DROPPED MY GLASSES - AND NOW I BET THEY'RE BROKEN!

NEVER FEAR!!

YOUR SPECS ARE BROKE BUT WORRY NOT. I'LL FIX THEM WITH MY MAGIC BOT!!

OH MAGIC CHEEKS AND MAGIC RING! MAKE GOOD ONCE MORE THIS BROKEN THING!
WHAT?

HELLO? WHAT'S GOING ON? IS SOMEBODY THERE? HELLO? WHAT ARE YOU DOING?
AH... ERM...

LATER...
HELLO - SOMETHING'S UP. WHAT'S THE MATTER?
WAH!

BOO HOO! I WANT TO LISTEN TO SHAKY ON THE RADIO - BUT THE BATTERIES ARE DEAD!
WHY THAT'S NOTHING TO CRY ABOUT!

BY THE POWER OF MY MAGIC BUM - BATTERIES FROM MY ARSE WILL COME!

OOOOF!!
Heave
Strain
GNN-N-NNG-G!

SILENCE
HMMM.

SHORTLY...
EXCUSE ME SONNY. HAVE YOU SEEN MY DOG? HE'S LOST.
CONCERN YOURSELF NOT!

AN OPTIC AID FROM UP MY BUM - WILL HELP YOU FIND YOUR CANINE CHUM!
OOER...
STICK YOUR HAND UP MY BEHIND. A TELESCOPE YOU'LL SURELY FIND!

OH I SAY...
OH DEAR...

HOY YOU! ARE YOU THE LAD WHO'S BEEN EXPOSING HIMSELF?
ERM...
WAIT THERE WHILE I CALL FOR ASSISTANCE!

phhoooph!
VERY QUIET SOUND

BAH! I'VE LOST THE PEA IN MY WHISTLE!
HAVE NO FEAR!

FROM MY ANUS I'LL PRODUCE A SHINY WHISTLE FOR YOUR USE!
CD·GPD·SD·ST·12·88

HERE - BLOW ON THIS!
THANKS SON.

PSQQWIRRRCH!!

# GORDON'S GRANDAD

YOUNG GORDON GATES WAS NOT PARTICULARLY REMARKABLE IN SO FAR AS HIS GRANDAD WAS IN NO WAY OUT OF THE ORDINARY!!

SPOILT
BASTARD

FOUR A.M.
WAKE UP FOR GOD'S SAKE WOMAN. ARE YOU GOING TO SLEEP ALL DAY?
IT IS MY BIRTHDAY AND I WANT MY PRESENTS!

PUFF! PANT!
BLINKING FLIP!! IS THAT ALL? I HOPE THEY'RE JUST MY SMALL PRESENTS!

I DON'T KNOW WHAT YOU THINK THIS IS, BUT I DON'T WANT IT! YOU REALLY HAVE NO IDEA, DO YOU?
WHAP!

JUST GO AND MAKE MY BREAKFAST!
YES, DEAR!
LISTEN, I KNOW YOU HATE ME BUT IT IS MY BIRTHDAY, GOD HELP ME!

SHORTLY...
MOTHER, THIS TONKER TRUCK ISN'T THE TOP OF THE RANGE...
OH, MY!
...AND I THOUGHT YOU LOVED ME!

I WON'T FORGET THIS, YOU!
WHEN YOU'RE DEAD I'M GOING TO DANCE ON YOUR GRAVE YOU HEARTLESS WITCH!

OH, MOTHER, I HATE YOU! I WAS SO LOOKING FORWARD TO TODAY AND NOW YOU'VE RUINED IT!
I'M SORRY TIMMY MY LITTLE CHERUB. DRY YOUR EYES, IT'LL SOON BE TIME FOR YOUR PARTY!

I DON'T WANT A PARTY! SCRUFFY CHILDREN WILL COME. THEY'LL BREAK MY TOYS AND I'LL GET NITS!
BUT THEY'VE ALREADY BEEN INVITED, DEAR, AND THEY'LL ALL BRING YOU A PRESENT!

SOON
DING DONG!!
I'LL GET IT!!
I'LL ONLY LET THEM IN IF THEY'VE BOUGHT LARGE PRESENTS!

FORM AN ORDERLY QUEUE FOR HEAVENS SAKE! DON'T PUSH!!
YES! THIS ONE'S LARGE ENOUGH! YOU CAN COME IN!

HAPPY BIRTHDAY, TIMMY! IT'S A PUPPET. I MADE IT ALL BY MYSELF!
I CAN SEE THAT!
PERHAPS YOU'D LIKE TO GET OUT AND COME BACK WHEN YOU'VE BOUGHT SOMETHING!

PRESENTLY...
HA! I LOVE PASS THE PARCEL! I'M BOUND TO WIN BECAUSE IT'S MY BIRTHDAY!
TEE! HEE! HEE!

BUT...
HOORAY! I'VE WON!

GIVE ME THAT PLANE! GIVE IT TO ME NOW YOU CHEAT!
IT'S MY BIRTHDAY!

THERE! THAT'LL TEACH YOU! CHEATS NEVER PROSPER!!
ANYWAY, IF I CAN'T HAVE IT, NOBODY CAN! SO THERE!!

SHORTLY...
TIME TO CUT THE CAKE, CHILDREN!
I'LL DO IT! YOU'LL CUT THE PIECES TOO BIG! BUT I WANT TO DO IT ON MY OWN! NOBODY CAN WATCH!
EVERYONE GET OUT! GO INTO THE KITCHEN AND I'LL CALL YOU WHEN I'VE FINISHED!

TWENTY MINUTES LATER...
TIMMY'S A LONG TIME CUTTING THE CAKE! I'LL SEE IF HE'S OKAY!

TIMMY!!
BARP!
COUGH!
G.P.D. ST. JS. CD. 1.89

AT FULCHESTER ROYAL INFIRMIRY...
EMERGENCY STOMACH PUMP ROOM
HA! IT WAS MY CAKE AND THEY DIDN'T GET ANY OF IT!

SID THE SEXIST
TITSOOT!

DINNER TIME...
POP STARS MAN SID - GOT WOMEN AROOND THEM LIKE FLIES ROOND A CAMEL'S ARSE ... IT'S CHURIZMA MAN, CHURIZMA.
IT'S AALL THEM TRENDY HAIRCUTS AN' THAT, MAN.
HMMM...

LATER...
ALAN
FRENCH UNISE
FOR CLASSY HAIRCU
OPE

IN A CLUB THAT NIGHT...
HEH! HEH!
HA! HA! HA! HA!
IT'S A FUCKIN' SHORT BACK AN' SLAP, MAN!
SLAP!
HO! HO! HO!
BATS!
HOWAY MAN! NAE BATS! NAE BATS!

BATS!
NAE REVENGIES!
FOT!
HEY, IT'S A FUCKIN' TUPENNY ALL-OFF!
A FUCKIN' SED NAE BATS! ... HOWAY LET'S SEE IF THIS'LL PULL OWT!

PHWOOAR! HEY LADS, THEZ A LASS OOT THERE GANNIN' LIKE A KANGAROO SHAGGIN' A SPACE-HOPPER!
WORRA MOOVA!

AN' IF SHE GANS LIKE THAT ON THE DANCEFLOOR - SHE'S A DORTY BEAST ON THE JOB!
OH AYE, HEY BAZ, SHE'S GIVIN' US A RIGHT TROUSER AROUSAL.

GERDOOT THERE AN' ASK 'ER TU DANCE MAN, SID.
A'LL NOT NEED TO MAN JOE, THIS HAIRCUT JUST RADIATES ANIMAL MAGNETISM AN' SEX AN' THAT.

DIVVEN' BE MICEY SID MAN, GAN AN ASK 'ER BEFORE YE LOSE YER CHANCE.
HOWAY MAN SID, YORRA BIG SKIPPIN' ROPE.
AYE, WI' FUCKIN' PINK HANDLES!

SID MAN, THE WORST THING THAT CAN HAPPEN IS SHE SEZ NO.

SO...
I-I-I-I'M WONDERING WHY...

...I STILL LOVE YOU

...JE NE SAIS PAS POURQUOI
POP!

IN CASUALTY...
WE'LL HAVE TO SHAVE YOUR HEAD BEFORE PUTTING THE STITCHES IN.
AIYAMAN! AIYAMAN! AIYA!

NEXT NIGHT...
GO ON SID, JUST TELL 'ER IT'S A NICE NIGHT OR SUMMIK.
BUT SHE'LL KNAA MAN - A LOOK DAFT.
DIVVEN'T BE STUPID MAN SID, Y'CANNAT TELL.

JUST SAY WORRA LOVELY MOON THERE IS MAN.
WELL... MEBEEZ...
GAN UUUURN MAN SID!

ERM... HELLO, WHAT A NICE NIGHT IT IS.
YES, LOVELY.

AYE... ERM AND WHAT A FULL MOON IN THE SKY.
YES, YOU'RE RIGHT. IT'S A SHAME TO BE INDOORS REALLY.

MIND PET, Y'DIVVENT SWEAT MUCH FOR A FAT LASS.

BIFF!
MMFF!

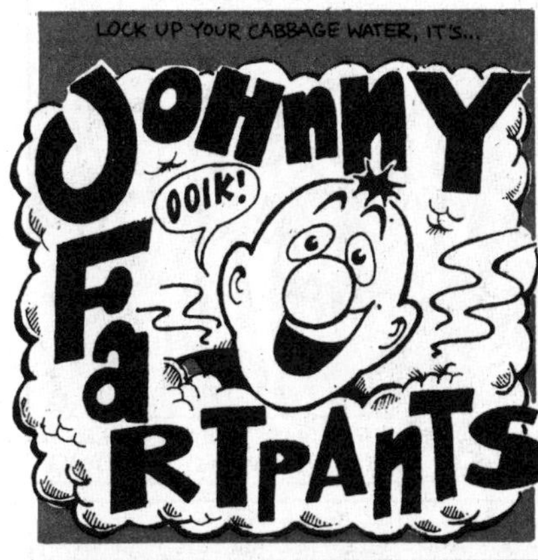
LOCK UP YOUR CABBAGE WATER, IT'S...
JOHNNY FARTPANTS
OOIK!

I'M OFF TO THE PARK ON MY NEW SCOOTER READERS!

IN THE PARK
OH MY! I CAN FEEL A REAL CLAPPER RATTLER COMING ON!
RUMBLE!
CHUGG!
QUAKE!
GLOP!

PWSHOOP!
OOH-ER!

I SAY, THAT'S THE FINEST EXAMPLE OF STUNT CYCLING I'VE EVER SEEN!
GRAND BMX COMPETITION
TODAY
?
HOORAY!

HERE'S YOUR PRIZE MONEY!
HO HO! NOW FOR A VERITABLE FEAST OF EGG-KEBABS AND TIZER!
£5

SOME TIME LATER, AT THE CAFÉ CHEZ VENT...
HERE IS YOUR BILL M'SIEUR!
OH DEAR, THERE MUST BE SOME MISTAKE, IT SAYS £100!

MAIS NON! THIS EEZ A NOUVELLE CUISINE RESTAURANT! THE PORTIONS ARE VERY VERY SMALL, AND VERY VERY EXPENSIVE M'SIEUR!
OH LUMME!

SO, IN THE KITCHENS...
BAH! ALL THE FOOD HAS HARDENED ONTO THESE POTS IN NO UNCERTAIN TERMS!

BUT BY CONVERTING THE POWER OF MY COUGHING COLON INTO A POWERFUL "SONIC BATH", USING A LENGTH OF STOUT CANVAS FIRE HOSE, THE JOB WILL BE DONE IN NO TIME.
FLUBBLE! UBBLE! UBBLE!

K-BOSH!
READER'S VOICE
OH NO! JOHNNY'S PUMP POWERED JACUZZI HAS BACKFIRED IN A VERY REAL SENSE!

I'D BETTER SCARPER BEFORE THE MANAGER NOTICES!

EXCUSE ME YOUNG MAN. MY DOG IS DAMP AND I FEAR HE MAY CATCH A COLD. COULD YOU DRY HIM OFF?
CERTAINLY!

YONKS! I THINK I OVER-COOKED IT THAT TIME!
QUOOFSH!
OH DEAR!
Shiloe ST. 89

MY DOG HAS EXPERIENCED THIRD DEGREE FLASH BURNS IN THE PUMP BLAST AND ALL HIS HAIR HAS FALLEN OUT. I DON'T WANT HIM ANYMORE. HERE, TAKE HIM TO THE DOG SHELTER.

SO...
OH NO! ALL THESE DOG'S NEED DE-LOUSING AND I'VE RUN OUT OF DOG-FLEA COMPOUND!
I'VE GOT AN IDEA!
DOG POUND

POOT!
COUGH!
YIP! YIP!
PARP!
YIP!
CHOKE!

OH LORDY—JOHNNY'S INADVERTENTLY KILLED ALL THE DOGS.
READER'S VOICE
NEVER MIND, THEY WERE GOING TO BE HUMANELY DESTROYED ANYWAY, YOU'VE SAVED ME THE BOTHER. HERE'S £100.
CHING!
RSPCA
£10

I'M FROM A DOG FOOD ADVERTISING COMPANY. THAT'S THE FINEST EXAMPLE OF A MEXICAN HAIRLESS I'VE SEEN, IDEAL FOR OUR BIG NEW CAMPAIGN.
TILT TILT
BIG BANK PLC
HERE'S £10,000

ALL THIS MONEY WILL PAY FOR THE DAMAGE YOUR "GENTLEMAN'S EXCUSE ME" DID TO MY RESTAURANT.
£10
CRIVENS!

BROWN BOTTLE
MEETS CIDER WOMAN AGAIN

THE SERENITY OF A SUNNY AFTERNOON IN FULCHESTER IS INTERUPTED AS POLICE ARE CALLED TO AN INCIDENT IN THE PARK...
NER NER!
NER NER!!

A CROWD OF ONLOOKERS HAS GATHERED
EXCUSE ME. LET US THROUGH. WE'RE POLICE OFFICERS!
COME ON. MOVE OUT OF THE WAY

WHAT IS IT?
EVERYBODY STAY BACK!
SERGEANT. YOU'D BETTER RADIO FOR URGENT ASSISTANCE!

IT'S CIDER WOMAN!!
AAAA...FUCK YERS AAAHL! Y'FRIGGIN BASTARDS! DIVVUN LOOK AT ME SON!!
COME ON Y'BASTARDS! GO AAAHN!! HAD AWAY N'SHITE Y'FRIGGERS!
Y'FUCKIN FRIGGERS! GE-AAARHGH!!

THE PARK IS EVACUATED WHILE POLICE CONSIDER THEIR NEXT MOVE

WE'VE SEALED OFF THE PARK COMPLETELY
GOOD. I DON'T WANT ANYONE GOING IN THERE. IT'S FAR TOO DANGEROUS!

SOONER OR LATER HER CIDER WILL RUN OUT AND SHE'LL FALL ASLEEP. THAT'S WHEN WE'LL MAKE OUR MOVE!
YA FUCKIN' FUCKAS!!
GO AAHN!
HOWAY Y'BASTARD!!
GEEEAARGH!!!

BUT NEARBY A YOUNG BOY HAS LOST HIS BALL...

HEY! GEEAAARGH!! CUM'ERE! CUM'ERE!! YOOOOH! CUM'ERE!

GIZ T-T-TEN PENCE WILL YA? F-FORRA CUP O'TEA
AAGH!! HELP!! HELP!!

WHAT'S HAPPENING?
OH NO!
SHE'S GOT A YOUNG BOY IN THERE WITH HER!!

HELLO? THIS IS AN EMERGENCY! WE'VE GOT A HOSTAGE SITUATION!

AND AT POLICE HQ...
THERE'S ONLY ONE THING FOR IT

IT'S TIME TO USE THE BOTTLE-PHONE!

IN A QUIET FULCHESTER SUBURB A PHONE RINGS AT THE HOME OF MILD MANNERED BANK CLERK BARRY BROWN
ISN'T THAT THE PHONE DEAR?
BRING! BRRING!!
ERM..YES. I'LL GET IT MOTHER

YES... SPEAKING... AT THE PARK?? RIGHT!!
I'M ON MY WAY!!

I'M JUST POPPING OUT TO THE SHOP FOR SOME MINTS MOTHER. I'LL NOT BE LONG
ALRIGHT DEAR. TAKE CARE

BUT UNKNOWN TO HIS MOTHER BARRY BROWN HAS OTHER PLANS
OFF LICENCE

HELLO AGAIN MR. BROWN. CRATE OF THE USUAL IS IT?
ERM... YES PLEASE

ARMED WITH A CRATE OF BEER BARRY BROWN HEADS FOR THE NEAREST PHONE BOX...
TELEPHONE
WHAT'S HE DOING IN THERE?

...AND EMERGES AS...
THE BROWN BOTTLE!!
YEEARGH!!!
HOWAY Y'B-BASTARDS! I'LL F-F-FUCKIN' TEK THE LOT O'YERS... Y'F-F-FUCKAHS!

OUR DRUNKEN HERO STAGGERS TO A NEARBY LOCK-UP GARAGE...
KAAHM-AAN Y B-B-BASTAAD!

...AND SECONDS LATER HE IS SPEEDING TOWARDS THE SCENE OF THE CRIME

CRASH!

WAAT THE F-F-F-FUCKIN' HELL?! J-J-J-JEEEZUS!! YAA F-FUCKIN B-B-BLIND OR WAAAT PAL??

FORTY-FIVE MINUTES LATER...
HEY LOOK! GETTING OUT OF THAT TAXI!
IT'S THE BROWN BOTTLE!
AND HE'S ARRIVED IN THE NICK OF TIME!

THAT'LL BE £3.50, PLUS AN EXTRA FIFTEEN QUID TO CLEAN UP ALL THAT PUKE OFF THE BACK SEAT!
EH? Y'WA?
FAACK AAAAF!! FRIGGIN F-F-F-F-FIFT-T-TEEN QUID!

BROWN BOTTLE! WE'RE SO GLAD YOU'RE HERE!
OOOAARH! ME F-FUCKIN HEED!
HEY, OFFICER! THIS BLOKE'S JUST PUKED IN MY CAB!!

THAT'S ALRIGHT SIR. WE'LL PAY FOR IT
RIGHT. THE SITUATION IS THIS...
WE HAVE CIDER WOMAN SURROUNDED IN THE PARK BUT THERE'S A BOY IN THERE WITH HER. WE DAREN'T MAKE A MOVE IN CASE SHE BECOMES VERBALLY ABUSIVE!

'ERE SON. GO AAAN! AVE A DRINK SON. GO AAAN!
ERM... NO THANKS BROWN BOTTLE
AAAAGH! GO AAHN SON! YER ME B-B-BEST FUCKIN' PAL... 'AVE SOME O'THIS!

ERM... LISTEN BROWN BOTTLE. ABOUT THIS HOSTAGE SITUATION
'EY!! WEZZ ME F-F-F M-M-M MATCHES?
S-S-S-SOME B-B-BAZDAZ NICKED ME FUCKIN' LIGHTA!

'ERE MATE! 'ERE MATE. GIZZ A LIGHT W-W-WILL YA?
CH-CH-CHEERS PAL!!
HIC!!

BROWN BOTTLE... ABOUT THIS HOSTAGE. IS THERE ANYTHING YOU CAN DO?
AYE SON...
L-L-L-LEAVE IT T-T-T-T'ME, P-P-PAL. NEY BOTHA!!

KAHMAHN!! Y B-B-BASTARDS! I'LL TEK THE F-F-FUCKIN' LOT O'YERS!!

HOWAY YA FAAAGHIN BAZTAZZ!! I'LL FUCKIN' TEK YERS AAL!!
HIC!! YA FACKIN' B-B-B-B-BAZTAZZ!!
BE CAREFUL BROWN BOTTLE!

RIP!
THUD!

KAAMAHN Y-BAZTAZZ!!
MIND THE LAKE BROWN BOTTLE!

SPLOSH!!

LATER...
IT'S A LUCKY THING THAT CIDER WOMAN FELL ASLEEP AND WE WERE ABLE TO RESCUE THE BOY UNHARMED
YES. YOU'RE PERFECTLY SAFE NOW SONNY!

HOW IS THE BROWN BOTTLE DOCTOR?
HE'LL BE OKAY. HE'S JUST SWALLOWED A BIT OF WATER THAT'S ALL. HE'S IN THE AMBULANCE RIGHT NOW

COR!! JUST WAIT TILL I TELL ALL MY PALS THAT I WAS RESCUED BY THE BROWN BOTTLE!
HIC! BLOOARRGH!!
THE END

What sort of person do you think you are? Attractive? Intelligent? Generous? Fun to be with? We'd all like to think so, wouldn't we. But no matter what we think of ourselves, others may see us differently. So how can you find out what kind of person you **REALLY** are?

One way to discover what sort of person you are is by asking yourself 'what am I like?' Because what you are like says a lot about the kind of person you are.

There are many signs and indicators that can reveal the true you. Here are just a few of them. Read them through and discover what sort of person you really are. You could be in for a surprise.

# What are you like?

## *What you are like says a lot about the kind of person you are*

*Girls! Here's a chance to win some make-up, a dress and a box of tampons. Just finish the following sentence using not more than 25 words.*

***"Bros are my fave group and I think Phillip Schofield is the dishiest guy on TV because..."***

*Send your answers on a postcard to 'Girls Competition', Viz, P.O. Box 1PT, Newcastle upon Tyne NE99 1PT. The best entry we receive will win the fab prize.*

★ **Are you a keen sports enthusiast who takes regular exercise? Perhaps you play tennis, go jogging, or train in a gym.**

You sound like the **athletic type.** You like to keep yourself physically fit by regularly exercising. You look after your body and enjoy playing sports.

★ **Are you top of your class – a real swot? Do you get good results in all your exams and always finish your homework on time?**

Then you must be an **intelligent,** academically minded person. You do well at school, always passing your exams. No doubt you'll end up with good qualifications.

★ **Do you collect pop records, go to concerts and pin pictures of your latest idol to the bedroom wall?**

You sound like a **pop fan** who enjoys listening to all the latest records by your favourite stars, and staring dreamy eyed at their pictures on your wall. You love music, enjoy going out and probably like dancing too.

★ **Do you often tell lies and deceive people, cheat in order to win at games and steal from others – even your friends?**

You are a **dishonest** person. You don't always tell the truth, and you'll go to any lengths to get your own way – even if it means cheating or stealing from a friend.

★ **Do you fall in love easily, only to find that it doesn't last?**

You're obviously one of life's **romantics** – the kind of person who falls in love easily, only to find that it doesn't last.

★ **Do you spend a lot of your time eating things, as a result of which you are overweight? Your idea of exercise is eating a large box of chocolates.**

If this is you then you are a **fat** person. This means that your bodyweight exceeds the norm for a person of your age, height and build, as it is compounded by excess fat. You probably wear large clothes and have difficulty getting into small spaces.

★ **Do you wear spectacles?**

If so you are the sort of person who has **bad eyesight.**

★ **Do you like to experiment with clothes and make-up, dressing slightly outrageously at parties, and have a pet rabbit.**

You obviously like to be slightly **different** – you don't follow the fashions, you make them! You don't like boring clothes, you prefer something slightly more outrageous. And you've got a pet rabbit.

SPOILT
BASTARD

ONE MORNING...
YOOO-HOOO! TIMMY, DEAR!
IT'S TIME MUMMY'S LITTLE ANGEL WAS DOWNSTAIRS HAVING HIS BREAKFAST!

COME ON, TIMMY DARLING
COUGH!

GOOD MORNING, MY PRINCE!
COUGH!
I'LL HAVE TO DRESS YOU QUICKLY TODAY, OR YOU'LL BE LATE FOR SCHOOL.

FOR GODS SAKE, WOMAN!
PUNT!
CAN'T YOU SEE I'M ILL? ARE YOU BLIND? ANY DECENT MOTHER WOULD KNOW WHEN HER CHILD WAS UNWELL, BUT NOT YOU, YOU HAG!

OH, MY GOD! WHAT HAVE I DONE? WHAT HAVE I DONE?
COUGH!
IF ANYTHING HAPPENS TO YOU I'LL NEVER FORGIVE MYSELF!

SHORTLY...
LET ME HAVE A LOOK AT THE THERMOMETER, POPPET!

HMM! IT LOOKS FINE, TIMMY, DEAR.
PERHAPS YOU'D FEEL BETTER IF YOU WENT TO SCHOOL.

GOD IN HEAVEN, I CAN HARDLY BELIEVE MY EARS! I'M DYING, YOU OLD BOOT!
THAT THERM-OMETER IS BROKEN! IF I GO OUT TODAY, I'LL CATCH PNEUM-ONIA AND DIE! IS THAT WHAT YOU WANT, WOMAN? WELL, IS IT?

IS IT?
NO, TREASURE, OF COURSE NOT
NOW LOOK WHAT I'VE DONE! I'VE GOT YOU ALL UPSET! LET ME MAKE YOU SOME BREAKFAST. YOU'LL FEEL BETTER IF YOU EAT SOMETHING.
A BOILED EGG, SOLDIERS, COCO POPS, CHOCOLATE BISCUITS AND LEMONADE!

AND MAKE SURE MY EGG IS SOFT BOILED, YOU DOZY OLD SOW! THREE MINUTES! IT'S NOT THAT DIFFICULT!
OF COURSE, MY PRECIOUS.
IT COULD BE THE LAST THING I EVER EAT!!

FIVE MINUTES LATER...
HERE WE ARE, DEAR!
WELL, IT'S NICE OF YOU TO FINALLY REMEMBER ME! I'VE ALMOST STARVED TO DEATH UP HERE!
COUGH!
LOOK AT ME! I'M AS WEAK AS A KITTEN! YOU'LL HAVE TO FEED ME!

BUT...
PTOO!

YOU IMBECILE! THAT EGG WAS SOFT BOILED!
BUT...BUT...
HAVEN'T YOU HEARD OF SALMONELLA POISONING? MY GOD! I CAN SEE IT NOW! YOU'RE TRYING TO MURDER ME!

ARRGH! GOD! I'VE GOT SALMONELLA! YOU GAVE IT TO ME, YOU WITCH!
OH! WHAT HAVE I DONE? I'LL GET A DOCTOR!
YOU EVIL OLD CRONE!

LATER...
WELL, MRS. TIMPSON...
...THERE'S NOTHING WRONG WITH YOUR SON THAT A GOOD SMACK ON THE BOTTOM WOULDN'T CURE!

IF HE GETS AWAY WITH THIS BEHAVIOUR ONCE, HE'LL DO IT AGAIN AND AGAIN!

SO...
TIMMY! TIMMY MY LITTLE PIXIE! THE DOCTOR SAYS YOU'VE BEEN PLAYING TRICKS ON YOUR MUMMY!

TIMMY!
HOW COULD YOU BE SO CARELESS, WOMAN? YOU LEFT TWO BOTTLES OF DOMESTOS WITHIN MY REACH! I THOUGHT THEY WERE LEMONADE!
BAAARP!
DOMESTOS
GPD·CD·89

I'VE DRUNK THE LOT, MOTHER, AND IT'S YOUR FAULT! I SUPPOSE YOU STILL EXPECT ME TO GO TO SCHOOL, DON'T YOU?

MR LOGIC
I THINK THEREFORE I AM...
A TWAT OF THE FIRST ORDER

BRRRRIIIIIING!
NATURALLY THE ALARM CLOCK TO AWAKEN ME.

HMMM... FASCINATING... I NOTE WITH INTEREST THAT MY GENERATIVE MEMBER IS NOT OCCUPYING IT'S ACCUSTOMED FLACID ATTITUDE.

I FEEL THE UNPRECEDENTED URGE TO TAKE PART IN HETEROSEXUAL INTERCOURSE AND HYPOTHESISE THAT SAID ACT WOULD BE A NOT UNPLEASURABLE ALTERNATIVE TO MASTURBATION. LACKING A COITAL PARTNER CONSEQUENTLY I MUST SEEK A COMPATIBLE SEXUAL COUNTERPART.
THIS WILL BE A MOST INTERESTING EXERCISE.

IN THE STREET...
GOOD DAY OFFICER... I AWOKE THIS MORNING IN A STATE OF SPONTANEOUS SEXUAL AROUSAL, AND, INTENT ON PROCURING CARNAL SATISFACTION I AM PRESENTLY ENDEAVOURING TO LOCATE A PROFESSIONAL COURTESAN WITH THE PURPOSE OF SECURING A CONTRACT FOR THE PROVISION OF FORNICATION.

DO YOU KNOW ANY PROSTITUTES?

CONSEQUENTLY...
LATER...
MADAME SOIXANTE-NEUF?... WOULD I BE CORRECT IN SURMISING THAT YOUR ADVERTISEMENT DOES NOT IN FACT APERTAIN TO THE PROVISION OF GALLIC LINGUISTIC EDUCATION, BUT IS IN FACT A THINLY VEILED OFFER FOR SEXUAL SERVICES IN RETURN FOR FINANCIAL OUTLAY?

SORRY LOVE I DON'T DO WEIRDOS AN' THAT...
... YOU'LL HAVE TO GET YOURSELF DOWN TO THE DOCKS TONIGHT.

THAT EVENING...
JUDGING BY HER OVERALL DEMEANOUR THE PROBABILITY IS THAT THIS WOMAN IS PLYING A SOLICITOUS TRADE. I WILL APPROACH HER AND INITIATE NEGOTIATIONS.

I AM DESIROUS OF SEXUAL CONGRESS TO WIT A CONJUGATION OF OUR SEXUAL ORGANS.
WHAT?

I AM PREPARED TO FURNISH MONETARY REMUNERATION CONSEQUENT UPON SUCCESSFUL PENETRATION.
YOU WANT A SHAG DO YOU LOVER?

AH YES, HOW FASCINATING, YOU USE A COLOQUIAL TERM. IN ORDER TO DEVELOP A PRODUCTIVE RAPPORT WITH YOU I WILL ADOPT A SIMILAR VOCABULARY.

WELL, ME OLD CHINA MUG, WHAT FISCAL DEMANDS WILL BE PLACED UPON ME FOR SAID SHAG? AND NO MISTAKE.
I DON'T KNOW WHAT YOU'RE ON ABOUT BUT IF YOU WANT OWT IT'S A TENNER FOR HAND RELIEF, THIRTY FOR ORAL, OR A PONY FOR A BONK.

WHAT AN UNUSUAL TARIFF SYSTEM. I AM NOT IN POSESSION OF ANY EQUINE LIVESTOCK. ASSUMING PLEASURE BE PROPORTIONAL TO COST AND NOTWITHSTANDING MY CAPITAL LIMITATIONS... hmmm...

YES, COUCHED IN YOUR DIALECTICAL VERBIAGE - A BLOW-JOB FOR SIX HUNDRED BOB-SHILLINGS WILL DO ME ALL RIGHT SATISFACTORILY CHEERS VERY MUCH GUV SQUIRE.

FURTHER ON...
WHO'S YOUR LADY FRIEND LAWRENCE? AREN'T YOU GOING TO INTRODUCE US THEN?
THIS IS A PROSTITUTE WHO WILL IN DUE COURSE BE PERFORMING ORAL STIMULATION OF MY PENIS.

?

SO...
hmmm... FASCINATING... FELATIO. I IMAGINE EJACULATION WILL COMMENCE PRESENTLY.

THE ALL NEW
Victor
AND HIS
BOA
CONSTRICTOR

VICTOR, YOUR GRAN HAS BEEN MISSING ALL DAY. IT WOULDN'T HAVE ANYTHING TO DO WITH THAT PESKY SNAKE OF YOURS, WOULD IT?
OOER!

BAH! I THOUGHT AS MUCH! THAT'S THE FIFTH RELATIVE IT'S EATEN THIS WEEK!
CRUMBS!

TAKE IT OUT AND GET RID OF IT. AND DON'T COME BACK UNTIL YOU'VE GOT A PROPER PET!
YES, MUM.

IT'S OKAY, BOA CONSTRICTOR! WE'LL JUST WALK AROUND FOR A WHILE!
WE'LL GO HOME WHEN SHE'S CALMED DOWN A BIT!

BAH! JUST MY LUCK! AN IMPORTANT MEETING TO GO TO AND MY BELT SNAPS.
HEY, HERE'S YOUR CHANCE TO DO A GOOD DEED, BOA CONSTRICTOR!

SO...
A FINE IDEA, SON. NOW I'LL MAKE THAT MEETING AFTER ALL!

!!

CRUMBS, YOU'VE SQUEEZED THE VERY LIFE OUT OF HIM. BAD CONSTRICTOR!
GASP!

LATER...
MEEOW!
BOO HOO! MY LITTLE CAT, TIDDLES, IS STUCK UP THAT TREE!

DON'T WORRY, MY SNAKE'LL BRING HIM DOWN!

RUSTLE
RUSTLE
MEE-OW

HRUMPH! A FAT LOT OF GOOD YOUR SNAKE TURNED OUT TO BE!
AHEM!
MEEOW!!

SHORTLY...
BLAST! YOU'VE BURST YOUR PADDLING POOL, SON! NOW WHAT ARE YOU GOING TO DO?
TO THE RESCUE!
FSSS!!

THANKS, VICTOR. YOUR SNAKE MAKES A FINE PADDLING POOL SUBSTITUTE!
YIPPEE!

BUT...
DADDY, MY PADDLING POOL IS GETTING SMALLER
OOER!

BAH! LOOK WHAT YOUR PESKY BOA CONSTRICTOR HAS DONE! I'M GOING TO HAVE TO GIVE YOU A GOOD THUMP!

LATER...
PERHAPS MUM WAS RIGHT! THIS SNAKE IS NOTHING BUT TROUBLE. I'M GOING TO GET MYSELF A PROPER PET!
PET SHOP
MR BO-JANGLES CHILDRENS ENTERTAINER MAGIC TRICKS BALOONS, ETC.
READERS' VOICE
BUT VICTOR, YOU'VE PASSED THE PET SHOP!

PRESENTLY...
MUM, I'M BACK! AND I'VE GOT A PROPER PET.

THIS IS FIDO!
AH, WHAT A LOVELY DOG! HE'LL BE ABLE TO PLAY WITH YOUR BABY BROTHER
WOOF!

WATCH OOT! IT'S THE
BACONS
WHO THE FUCK ARE YOU LOOKIN' AT?
BIFFA
YOU TELL 'EM BIFFA SON
MUTHA
FATHA

THE BACONS ARE GOING TO THE SEASIDE
REET! I'VE GOT ME PAPER, ME BEER AN' SOME TABS. IS THERE OWT ELSE WE'VE FORGOT?
FATHA

AH! I'VE FORGET ME HAMMA. GAN 'AN' GERRIT FORRUS WILL YA BIFFA?
FATHA
ALREET FATHA

HERE FATHA

SMACK!

HERE. Y'CAN PUT THE FUCKA BACK NOO
FATHA
BASTARD!

AT WHITLEY BAY...
HOWAY, LET'S GAN ON THE BEACH!

HEY, YOOZ. WE WAS 'ERE FIRST. **CLEAR OFF!**
WHAT?

COME ON NOW! SURELY THERE'S ENOUGH ROOM ON THE BEACH FOR EVERYONE TO ENJOY THEMSELVES
GAN ON BIFFA!
SAVE TREES WHALES OZONES ETC.
THERE'S NO NEED TO ADOPT SUCH A CONFRONTATIONAL ATTITUDE

WHACK!
UMFF!
SAVE TREES WHALES OZONES ETC.

ARE YOU ALRIGHT ROLAND?
YES MEGAN. COME ON, WE SHALL REPORT THIS TO THE APPROPRIATE AUTHORITIES...

LATER...
HOWAY FATHA, LET'S BUILD A SANDCASTLE
FUCK OFF SON. I'M BUSY.

HERE SON... YA MUTHA'LL HELP Y'BUILD A SANDCASTLE
WILL YA?!

WILL A FUCK!!
PRANG!!
OOOF!!

NOW FRIG OFF AN' LEAVE US ALAIRN!
AYE SON, HADAWAY AN' SHITE!

THIS IS BORIN'. THERE'S NOWT T'DEE!!

HEY! A BOTTLE WASHED UP ON THE SHORE!

OOH... AN' THERE'S A MESSAGE IN IT!!

POP!

HOWAY BIFFA. WE'RE GANNIN' FOR SOME FISH N' CHIPS

FISH N' CHIPS THREE TIMES, PAL
AYE, WI' PLENTY O' FUCKIN' CHIPS
AN' EXTRA BATTER ON MINE
FISH 'N' CHI
CERTAINLY SIR
HEY! I LOVE FISH N' CHIPS, ME

THERE YOU ARE. THAT'S £4.05
HEY! IT LOOKS FUCKIN' LOVELY FATHA
CHEERS PAL!

OOH HEY! IT SMELLS GOOD AN' ALL
AYE BIFFA. THIS ONE'S YOURS SON.
I DO HOPE YOU ENJOY IT...

SPLAT!
OOOFF!!

HEY, THIS IS FUCKIN' LOVELY, INNIT MUTHA
AYE. IT'S FUCKIN' CHAMPION
BASTARDS!

SOON...
SPANISH CITY
HOWAY! LET'S GAN IN 'ERE

ROLL UP, ROLL UP. RING THE BELL AND WIN A PRIZE. HOW ABOUT YOU SIR? 25p A GO.
RING THE BELL AND WIN A GOLDFISH
HOWAY FATHA. LET'S HAVE A GAN ON THIS!

CLANG!!

GAN ON FATHA. BEAT THAT!

WALLOP!
OOYAH!!

HA HA HA! SEE YA LATER BIFFA
BASTARD!

I SAY! I SAW YOU RING THAT BELL EARLIER. I THINK I MIGHT HAVE JUST THE JOB FOR YOU!
EH?

PRESENTLY...
ROLL UP! ROLL UP! STEP RIGHT THIS WAY!
SO HE THINKS HE'S FUCKIN' HARD DOES HE?
I'LL KNOCK HIS TEETH OOT, ME.
AYE, HE'S FUCKIN' DEED!
LERRUS A'RIM!
PAY HERE
GO 3 ROUNDS WITH BIFFA AND WIN £25
I'LL BREAK HIS FRIGGIN' ARSE!

INSIDE...
BOOF!

WHACK!
ANOTHER KNOCKOUT FOR BIFFA!

HEH HEH HEH! THIS IS FUN
WHO'S NEXT?!

ME, BIFFA.
OOH FUCK...

BLAM!

SID THE SEXIST
TITS OOT!

HOW MAN SID, PUT YER EYES BACK IN YA HEED - AALL THAT BARMAIDS GANNA PULL FU YE IS A PINT!
AYE SID, FERGERRIT MAN, HEV A BASH AT SOME LASSES ROOND THE BAR!

PHWOOAR HEY! WHAT COULD YE DE WI' THAT, EH LADS?
I DIVVEN'T KNAA, MEBEEZ IT NEEDS SOME WATTER OR SUMMIK.
ITS FLAT MAN BOB. ASK THEM TU PULL ANOTHER ONE FOR YU.

YA DURZY BASTADS!
HE WUZ TAALKIN' ABOOT THAT LASS - HEY MAN WATCH ME TACTICS - I'M GANNA MOOVE IN.

HOW PET, D'YU LIKE JEWELLERY?
WHY? GOING TO BUY ME A RING, ARE YOU?
NO, BUT YOU CAN SUCK ME COCK, IT'S A GEM!

POIK!
AAAAAAAAAA

WHORRID Y'DE THAT FOR? ARE YU A LEZZA OR SUMMIK?
YOU WORM.

SHALL WU GEROOT O' THIS BAR LADS OR WHAT?
AYE, HOWAY LADS, WE'LL GERRUP THE TOON MOOR, EH?
SOUND IDEA, BUSH AALL AWA UP THERE!
THE HOPPIN'S - FUCKIN' MAGIC!

THE HOPPIN'S? FUN FAIRS IS FER BAIRNS, MAN!

HEY, SID'S NEVER SCARED O' GANNIN' ON THE RIDES THO' IS 'E?
DIVVEN'T TAALK YA SHITE!

TITTER! SMIRK!
GIGGLE!
TITTER!

SHADDAP! A'M FUCKIN' WELL NOT!
HE FUCKIN' IS THO'!
ARE Y' 'STARTIN' LIKE?
WORRIFF I AM LIKE?
HAWAY THEN!

SOME TIME LATER...

LADS! LASSES OOTSIDE THE GHURST TRAIN, LET'S GAN IN-TU IMPRESS THEM!
AYE! WE CAN COME OOT AN' SAY IT WUZ SHITE AND THE'LL THINK WE'RE ROCK!

W-WHORRABOOT T-THE HALL OF M-M-MIRRORS-THAT'LL IM-IMPRESS 'EM!
CHATTER! TREMBLE!

GHOST TRAIN
HOWAY IN MAN SID, Y'BIG POOF!
YANK!
ERK!

MINUTES LATER...
REET... MEK SOME NOISE!
HEY, THAT WOULDN'T SCARE NEE-ONE!
WOULDN'T SCARE A BAIRN EH, SID?
WHINE!
HEE! HEE!
TEE! HEE!

HEY LADS, CAN YUZ SMELL SUMMIK?
WHORRA FUCKIN' HUM!
?
WAFT!
AAH, WHY DID A HEV TU WEAR ME WHITE BREEKS?

HA! HA! HA! SID'S FUCKIN' PAPPERED HESEL'!
OAAH, MEBEEZ A ETT SUMMIK... NAR-SERIOUSLY LADS!...
ming!
SCAREDY-CAT! SCAREDY-CAT!

JUST THEN...
HEY, YOU. ME MATE WON'T COME ON THE BIG WHEEL WITH US - WILL YOU COME INSTEAD?
GUMPH!

AYE, OF COURSE HE WILL PET!
AAH, HOWAY LADS!
KEEP 'ER TAALKIN' SID, SHE'LL NEVER NURTICE!
HO! HO!
HA! HA!
HEH! HEH!
COME ALONG, THERE'S NOTHING TO BE SCARED OF!

EVENTUALLY...
HEY PET, I'M SORRY LIKE. IT MUST BE SUMMIK A ETT Y'KNAA, HEY A MEAN IT'S NOT THAT A WUZ SCARED OR OWT... HEY AN' A'VE HED NOWT TU DRINK Y'KAA...
BIG WHEEL
JESUS. WHAT A TWAT.

# Postman Plod

## The Miserable Bastard

# Roger Mellie

## The Man On The Telly

HAVE YOU FORGOTTEN ALREADY? YOU SAID WE WERE GOING TO BRIGHTON TODAY
YES...
... BUT WE'RE GOING THERE TO COVER THE ANNUAL SOCIALIST AND LIBERAL DEMOCRAT PARTY'S CONFERENCE, NOT TO GO SUNBATHING!!

THE POWER OF LOVE
Love seemed light years away for young Julie Thompson, or so it seemed. Or was it? Little did she imagine how her lonely, lovelorn life was to change one night. One night, as she gazed from her bedroom window, the stars in the lonely night sky seemed to echo the tears that tore like knives through her heart . . .
Suddenly something caught her eye . . .
GOSH! A FALLING STAR! HOW BEAUTIFUL!
I MUST MAKE A WISH QUICKLY!
I WISH THERE WAS SOMEONE IN MY LIFE. . .
SOMEONE I COULD LOVE, AND WHO WOULD LOVE ME ALSO . . .
But as the glow of the falling star faded into darkness, so did the embers of Julie's dreams of love and companionship.
PERHAPS I'LL NEVER FIND TRUE HAPPINESS.
The next morning, Julie was making her way to the launderette . . .
EXCUSE ME, ARE YOU ROMANTICALLY INVOLVED PRESENTLY?
WHAT AN UNUSUAL QUESTION — BUT I DO FIND HIS CANDID APPROACH DISPLAYS A REFRESHING HONESTY.
I WOULD LIKE TO FALL IN LOVE WITH YOU PLEASE.
GASP!
DON'T YOU THINK YOU'RE BEING A BIT HASTY? PERHAPS WE SHOULD MEET AGAIN TOMORROW, AND GET TO KNOW EACH OTHER A LITTLE BETTER.
VERY WELL
BY THE WAY, MY NAME'S J . . . HUNH!
But the mysterious stranger had vanished as strangely as he had appeared.

The next day . . .
COOOEEE! . . . ERM! HEY — IT'S STRANGE, WE'RE GOING OUT TOGETHER AND I DON'T EVEN KNOW YOUR NAME!
I AM NAMRON 7
WHAT AN UNUSUAL NAME.
PRELIMINARIES ARE CONCLUDED. LET US COMMENCE.
TELL ME, NAMRON 7, TELL ME ABOUT YOUR HOME.
I AM FROM A PLACE VERY FAR AWAY.
YOUR TALES OF FAR LANDS ARE SO FASCINATING, NAMRON 7. BUT WHAT OF YOUR FAMILY?
I HAVE NO FAMILY. NEVER ASK ME THAT QUESTION AGAIN.
OH NAMRON 7. I'M HAVING SUCH A LOVELY TIME!
Julie seemed to have found a companion . . . someone she could talk to. Someone who could share her hopes and dreams. Someone to laugh with, someone to cry with.
AT LAST, I THINK I'VE FOUND A COMPANION. SOMEONE I CAN TALK TO. SOMEONE TO SHARE MY HOPES AND DREAMS. SOMEONE TO LAUGH WITH, SOMEONE TO CRY WITH.
NAMRON 7 . . . I . . . I . . . I THINK I LOVE YOU.
EXCELLENT. I MUST LEAVE NOW
BUT WHEN SHALL I SEE YOU AG . . .
But Namron 7 was nowhere to be seen.
As Julie made her way home, she was in a state of confusion, emotionally.
I SO MUCH WANT TO SEE NAMRON 7 AGAIN. I'VE BEEN WAITING ALL MY LIFE FOR SOMEONE LIKE HIM. HE'S A KIND OF STRANGE AND WONDERFUL KIND OF GUY.

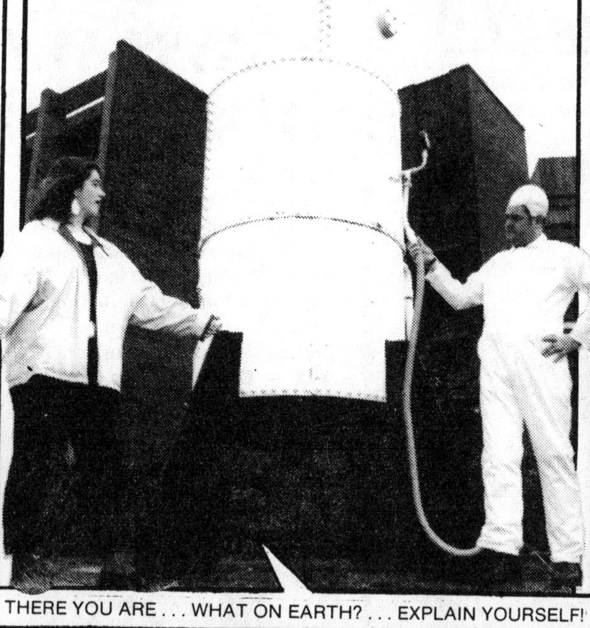


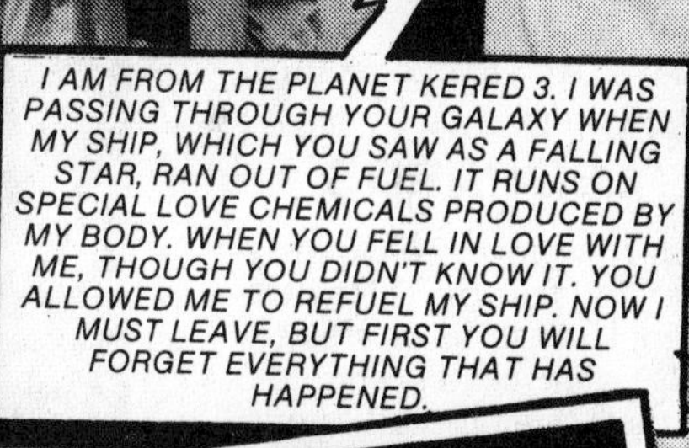


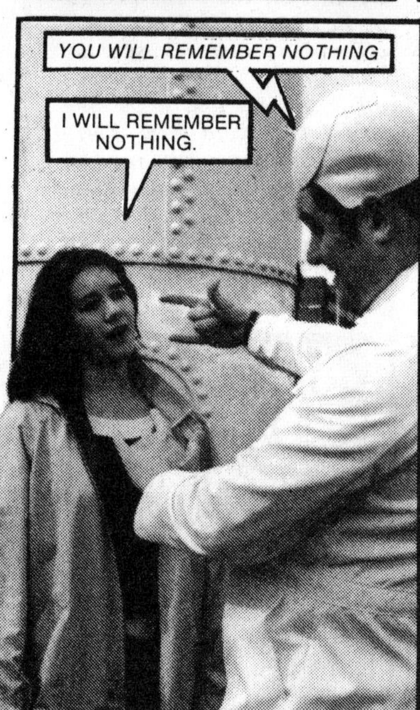

THE END.

SD ST Photography by C Davison 5.89 Spaceship furnished by Dr Hans Zarkov

**Gotcha! We expose Britain's latest celebrity tax dodge!**

# ANIMAL CRACKERS!

## Top stars queue up to buy wildebeests, gnus, stoats and platypi

Some sheep yesterday

**Showbiz celebrities are stocking up on pets in order to avoid paying tax! And the homes of many of todays top stars are beginning to resemble zoos, with more and more animals being purchased in this latest bid to beat the taxman.**

A couple of years ago big money earners like Steve Davis, Terry Wogan and Cliff Richard were investing in trees in an attempt to foil the Inland Revenue. But the government acted swiftly to close that loophole, and the word from top financial pundits is now "Buy Animals".

### SNAKES

The animals involved range from traditional household pets to more exotic creatures such as snakes, monkeys and even kangaroos. And delighted pet shop owners have never had it so good. They report that wealthy stars are buying anything they can get their hands on.

"I've sold over 200 parrots this week", one shop-keeper told us. "And I've got another 125 on order".

### LEOPARDS

Even zoos have been approached by frantic celebrities trying to cash in on this tax dodge. One head keeper told us that several well-known TV personalities had offered him cash in exchange for animals, including leopards, elephants and giraffes.

### BANDICOOTS

Tax advisor Kenneth McBride, believes that more and more highly paid show business celebrities, sportsmen and pop stars will soon be jumping on

## Latest tax dodge leaves investors 'squids in'

the animal bandwagon. "It may sound like a risky investment, but the savings that are there to be made are enormous. Over twelve months a top earner like Radio DJ Simon Bates could save anything up to half a million pounds in tax by spending the money, for example, on water buffalow".

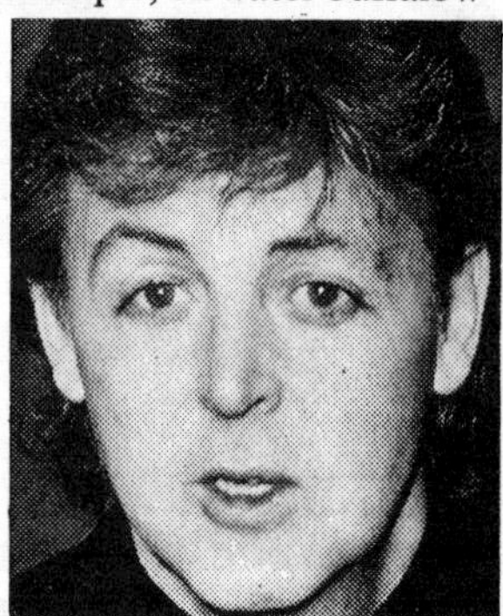

McCartney — crocodiles.

A government spokesman told us that whilst buying animals was not illegal, many required licences, and were not suitable as household pets. He admitted that the government would be keeping an eye on the situation.

## THEY'LL TRY ANYTHING TO BEAT THE TAXMAN!

**Until recently top celebrities and money earners could expect to loose over half their income in tax. And even now stars like Shakin' Stevens must hand over 40p in tax for every pound they earn. Here are just some of the tactics — successful or otherwise — that have been tried in order to beat the taxman.**

*£ Pop star, Leo Sayer, a big money earner in the 70's, took his accountant's advice and lived in a hammock in his back garden for twelve months, never once setting foot on the ground. But the stunt failed, and Sayer was left with back-ache – and a tax bill of over £50,000!*

*£ Mick Jagger, a millionaire several times over, eventually moved to France to avoid UK taxes. But not before he had tried several more bizarre methods. One plan, to live in a submarine in the River Thames near Oxford, failed when the vessel sprang a leak. When Jagger eventually surfaced, tax inspectors were waiting to present him with a bill – for £750 million.*

*£ Crafty pop star Kylie Minogue came up with a brilliant scheme to beat the Australian taxman. The singer ordered a tanker load of milk from a dairy in the USA. By the time the vessel arrived in Australia the milk had gone off, and so the entire cost of the operation – $1 million – was offset against tax. Later, the ship returned to New York, and during the stormy voyage, the cargo turned into cheese. The ingenious singer then sold the lot – at a profit of over $10 million!*

## FAMOUS PEOPLE ON THE TOILET

# Billy the Fish

ONCE MIGHTY FULCHESTER UTD. NOW STRUGGLING AT THE FOOT OF THE 4th DIVISION, HAVE BEEN DRAWN AWAY IN THE FIRST ROUND OF THE F.A. CUP TO NON-LEAGUE NO-HOPERS SUDLEY LANE PAPERBOYS!

**WHO** HAS **STOLEN** THE MONEY, AND **CAN** IT BE **RECOVERED** IN TIME TO **SAVE** THE CLUB? **IS THIS THE END** FOR FULCHESTER, **OR** WHAT?

# IT'S THE PAGE THA

## 'Thanks' for helping to pick up my oranges

Thanks to the many passers by who helped me to pick up the bag of oranges which I dropped while shopping on Dewsbury High Street last Wednesday afternoon. I was unable to thank them all fully at the time, but their generous help was much appreciated.

At the final count I had recovered 5 of the 6 oranges which I had purchased. The sixth was damaged by a passing car. Thanks once again to all those who helped.

Mrs B. Johnson
Dewsbury

## Magical memories

**I am 93 and can still remember when butter was tuppence a pound.**

**Mr. M Knox**
**Edinburgh**

**My wife and I have been married for over 30 years, but I will never forget the day we were married. It was a Saturday.**

**M Error**
**Battersea**

I was really worried the other day when I saw a ticket inspector getting on the train — I didn't have a ticket. Then suddenly I remembered I didn't need one. I was the driver.

D. Woods
Romford

## My hat is too big

My hat is too big. Any big headed readers care to swap?

Tim Scott
Northwich

****Do any other readers have items which they no longer use and would like to swap for something else? If so drop us a line. Please mark your envelope 'I've got an item I no longer use and would like to swap for something else'.***

I have a hair dryer and a set of curling tongs that I'd like to swap for an electronic calculator and a purse with a clip fastening.

Mrs. T. Cassidy
York

I recently began collecting beer mats and already have four. Two are the same, however. Would any readers care to swap?

J Smith
Dover

## Hubby's car mystery

The other day my husband called the police when he awoke to find that our car was not in its usual parking place outside our house. We had to laugh though later we remembered what we'd done. My husband had built a small garage at the side of our house the previous day, and we had parked the car inside it that evening.

Needless to say the police, who spent several hours searching for the car, were not quite so amused.

Mrs M. MacDonald
Luton

Sitting at the breakfast table the other day, I mentioned to my wife what a fabulous band Genesis were. "You would say that," she replied. "You're the lead singer." I had to laugh, because it was true.

Phil Collins
Surrey

Last night my wife worked late and her kind-hearted boss invited her back to his house for a meal. He even treated her to a bottle of champagne. How generous it was of him—rarely do you hear of such kindly behaviour by an employer these days.

My wife, however, must have felt pretty foolish. For on her return, I pointed out that she had been wearing her dress inside out.

R.W.
Leicester

I have been plagued with back trouble throughout my adult years, yet never once have I complained.

Dennis Nails
Wakefield

## Service with a smile

The other day my daughter and I were on a shopping trip to Plymouth when the train we were travelling on was involved in a collision. I couldn't help laughing, as we lay trapped in the wreckage, when the steward's voice came over the annoucement system. "Apologies for the delay", he quipped. "The fire brigade are on their way, but in the meantime the buffet will remain open for the sale of tea, coffee, hot and cold snacks etc." It's good to know that some British Rail employees do have a sense of humour.

Mrs D. Craig
St. Agnes

Children say the funniest things, and often at the most awkward moments. The other day I was invited to Buckingham Palace to receive a medal from the Queen. "Where shall I stick it?" she asked, wondering where to pin the medal.

"Up your arse", said my 5 year old son, quick as a flash. My face went bright purple, and not surprisingly, I wasn't given the medal after all.

Mrs T. Hibbitt
Leeds

## Mollie Sugden's

## Plastering Tips

### 1. Repairing small cracks

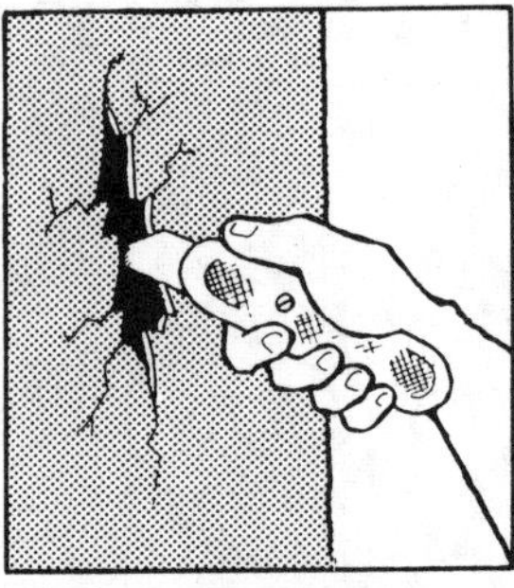

**Mollie says:** "Remove any loose flakes of plaster from around the crack, even if it means making the hole larger. Use a Stanley knife or a stout screwdriver."

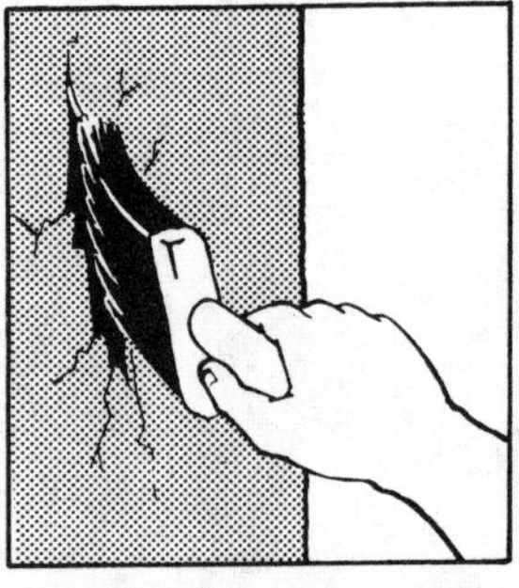

"Apply water to the crack liberally with a brush. This will prevent the old plaster soaking up the water from the new."

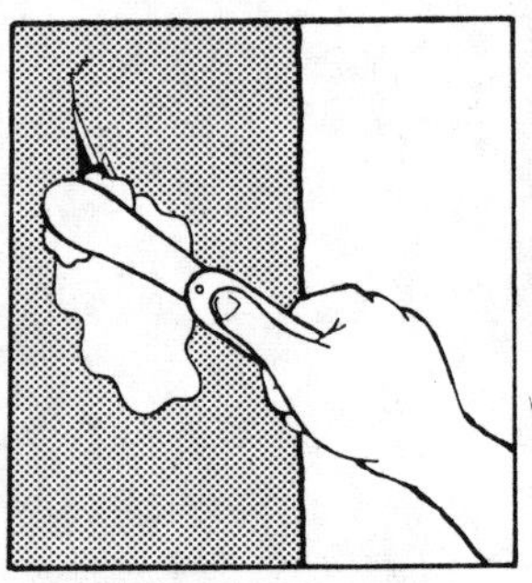

"Using a palate knife, fill the hole with your filling compound. Pack it in well. There are many 'ready mixed' fillers on the market."

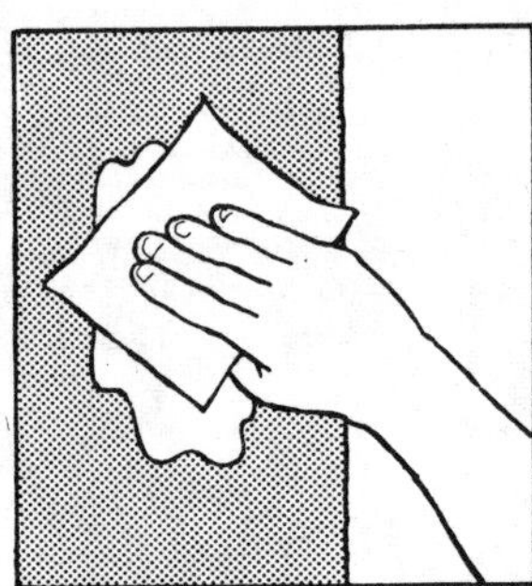

"Leave to dry for 24 hours, before sanding **Take a tip from Mollie:** "For a truly professional finish you may like to paint the plastered area the same colour as the surrounding wall."

## 'S THE RAGE IN THIS DAY AND AGE

## Can anyone help?

I often have trouble remembering what the traffic light colours mean, and this can often prove dangerous. Do your readers have any suggestions which would help me remember the meanings?

J Webber
Nottingham

In answer to Mr. Webber's letter (this issue), I am a greengrocer and I find it useful to associate the lights with similar coloured fruits. The red light is like a tomato, the first two letters of which are found in the word 'STOP'. Amber is like a lemon, which ends in the letter 'N' as does 'SLOW DOWN'. Finally, green is like a gooseberry, the first two letters of which spell 'GO'. Simple.

G. Sprake
Guisley

I find a useful way to remember what the traffic lights mean is to say this little rhyme to yourself as you approach:

When the red light does shine,
I must stop on the line,
When the amber is there,
Then I'd better take care,
But when the green light does show,
Then off I may go.

P. Madeley
Rawdon

**AVOID losing children in dark, crowded places by painting them with luminous paint.**

**J. D. Radley**
**Worcester**

**LADIES. A toilet freshener in your handbag helps keep it smelling fresh.**

**Jackie P.**
**Bolton**

**CUT laundry bills. Tie your dirty linen to the roof rack when you next visit the car wash.**

**R. Hughes**
**Mid-Glamorgan**

**WHEN children outgrow their potty they make attractive fruit bowls and are much cheaper and more attractive than the ones sold in shops.**

**J. Moy**
**Hull**

**KEEP a tin of red paint in your car. If you see a motor accident you can then pour it over yourself and pretend to be involved.**

**J. Mitchell**
**Southampton**

**PUTTING just the right amount of gin in the goldfish bowl makes the fishes' eyes bulge and they swim in an amusing way.**

**Magnus Macintyre**
**Oxford**

**A SMALL hole cut out of a window will allow your budgie to come and go as it pleases.**

**C. Press**
**Manchester**

**STOP birds nesting in your garden by collecting all the twigs and moss in the neighbourhood and hiding them in your shed.**

**P. Reaney**
**Rothwell**

**I SEW a few figs into the turn-ups of my husband's trousers and he has never had piles.**

**Mrs. T. Yorath**
**Carlisle**

**SAVE time when crossing a one way street by only looking in the direction of the oncoming traffic.**

**D. Rogers**
**Hemel Hempstead**

**DISTINGUISH microwave ovens from TV sets at a glance by cutting out the letter 'M' in brightly coloured paper and affixing it to the door of the oven.**

**Mrs G. Jones**
**Leicester**

**WHEN crossing a one-way street, always look for traffic in both directions in case a large, blue furniture removal lorry is reversing the wrong way up the road.**

**D. Rogers**
**Hemel Hempstead**
**General Infirmary**

**STOP squirrels and birds taking food from the bird table by first placing it in a biscuit tin and securing it with heavy duty tape.**

**P. Reaney**
**Rothwell**

**RIGHT-HANDED people. Perform everyday tasks with your left hand so that when you get a splinter, you can carefully remove it using your right hand.**

**A. Pryde**
**Bromley**

**I SLEEP with a large key under my tongue and I never suffer from cramp.**

**Mrs. T. Yorath**
**Carlisle**

**PREVENT bees and butterflies stealing your pollen by enclosing each flower head in a plastic bag securely fastened around the stem with a clothes peg.**

**P. Reaney**
**Rothwell**

**AVOID embarrassing yourself when drunk by first driving to an abandoned woodshed with the booze in your boot and drinking it there.**

**B. and D.**
**Bristol**

**EVERYDAY, make a list of everything you do and hand it in at your local police station. That way, you can easily be eliminated from their enquiries in the event of a crime.**

**D. Anon**
**Monkchester**

# T.V. STARS DICE WITH DEATH!

## *-claims shock report*

**TV's top game show hosts are putting their lives at risk, due to a lack of knowledge of basic emergency survival techniques, claims a report out today. And if disaster struck tomorrow, many of TV's top names such as Bruce Forsyth and Les Dawson could be among the first to perish.**

The report reveals how many celebrities:

* **DON'T KNOW** how to erect a survival shelter.
* Are **UNABLE** to navigate using the stars.
* **CANNOT** trap and skin a rabbit.

Author of the report Major Geoffrey Patterson-Smythe confessed to being "alarmed" by widespread apathy towards survival training within TV light entertainment in general.

### TV COMPANIES

"It's up to the Government and the TV companies to take steps to improve the situation. It's no good putting it off — tomorrow could be too late".

Among proposed improvements put forward in the report are compulsory survival training courses for all TV personalities, and random 'spot checks' which would be carried out by the IBA to ensure that standards of survival training were being maintained. "Celebrities could be asked to distinguish between poisonous and non-poisonous berries, for example, or given a limited period of time in which to construct an improvised stretcher for use in an emergency, using only the branches from a tree", the Major told us.

### TV COMPANY

However, a spokesman for one TV company who we contacted said that they will not be taking up the new proposals. "This sounds like scaremongering to me", he told us. Several game show hosts who we asked to speak to were yesterday 'unavailable for comment'.

Sex earthquake rocks quiet village

# I made love to myself ~ while I watched

**A 42 year old man has revealed how he made love to himself while his wife slept nearby.**

And Reginald Thompson has stunned neighbours in the quiet village of Banwell with his saucy revelations. "He seemed so quiet", one neighbour told us last night.

## Village torn apart by torrid sex tornado

The house in Banwell where Thompson's sordid sex sessions took place.

### FROLICS

Reg's sexy frolics with himself began one night in 1986 after he had spent a quiet evening at home with his wife, Carol. "Carol had gone to bed early and I was alone on the settee", he told us. "I'd had a few drinks and I was feeling very relaxed. The next thing I knew I felt my hand on my shoulder. Seconds later I was rolling around naked on the floor with myself. It seemed like the most natural thing in the world".

Reg began to have regular solo sex sessions whenever his wife was out of the house. "One minute I'd be in the garden mowing the lawn, and the next minute I'd be in the shed, fondling my own buttocks", he revealed.

## Passion volcano erupts showering village with red hot love lava

On one occasion, Reg sat and watched while he made love to himself. "I'd just drunk a bottle of Vodka and was feeling uninhibited. I sat and watched myself in the mirror. It was a fantastic experience, although I had a headache afterwards". Soon Reg was having sex with himself up to three or four times a week. "Sometimes I would just sit in the cupboard under the stairs with my hand on my knee. At other times, I would roll around on the carpet in front of the fire for hours on end. On one occasion, I even knocked the coffee table over and spilt a glass of wine. I only just managed to clean it up before my wife got home".

### SESSIONS

Locals at the Kings Head Hotel only 200 yards from the Thompson's semi-detached house, were shocked whey they heard of Reg's steamy sex sessions. "He seemed so quiet", one customer told us.

# TIPTON IS TOP FOR TOURISM

**Ask any discerning holiday-maker where he's heading this Summer — and the answer won't be Benidorm, Bermuda or Barbados. It will be Tipton!**

This is the astonishing claim made by Mr Hugo Guthrie, chairman of the Tipton Borough Council Committee on Tourism. And he believes that 'Terrific Tipton' will soon be top of the tourist tree.

"At Tipton we have a comprehensive range of amenities to suit holidaymakers of all ages. There's truly something for everyone at Tipton. We've got some smashing countryside with marvellous views only 20 miles the other side of Wolverhampton".

"And for the water sports enthusiast, we've got a very pleasant stretch of river, and plenty of canals. And did you know incidentally, that here in Tipton there are more miles of canal than there are in Stourbridge. Indeed, Tipton has been described as the Venice of the West Midlands".

## Tip Top Tipton Tipped as Top Tourist Trap

And according to Mr Guthrie, Tipton certainly isn't lacking in nightlife. "Appearing for the whole Summer season at the Tipton Apollo Theatre, we hope to have the one and only Bernie Clifton and his Comedy Ostrich — as seen on TV".

### BOOK EARLY

Holiday-makers intending to visit Tipton are advised to book early, as accommodation will be in short supply. And a final word from Mr Guthrie — he believes Tipton's attractive new tourist slogan says it all. "Tipton — it's terrific".

# WE'RE SKINT, M'LUD!

## Top lawyers plead poverty

**Many top lawyers are having to take on part-time jobs in order to make ends meet. Highly trained barristers and top solicitors are resorting to bar jobs and part-time restaurant work in order to boost their paltry income.**

### GET BY

**One solicitor we spoke to said he worked Saturday mornings collecting litter at MacDonald's restaurant in London's Piccadily, as well as delivering free newspapers during the evenings. "I still find it hard to get by", he told us. "A colleague has resorted to advertising his services in newsagent's windows as a part-time gardener and handyman", he added.**

### SURVIVE

**Top lawyers feel that with rising mortgage rates and inflation, it's not possible for them to survive charging only £120 per hour for their services. "Unless there is a dramatic increase in our levels of pay, I can see ugly scenes reminiscent of the miners strike breaking out in the Court rooms and the offices of the legal profession", one told us this morning.**

# MAN 'HAD SEX WITH 2,500 WOMEN' ~claim

A Northampton man is claiming to have had sex with 2,500 women over the last five years.

### Probably

"Come to think of it, it was probably more like 3,000", he told us yesterday.

SPOILT
BASTARD
AT THE SEASIDE...
HURRY UP WOMAN! IT IS MY HOLIDAY TOO. THERE ARE LOTS MORE SHOPS DOWN THERE AND I WANT THINGS!

GIVE ME SOME MONEY. I WANT A GO ON THAT TELESCOPE!
WELL, COME ON!
BUT TIMMY, MY CHERUB. IT'S SO MISTY AT SEA TODAY. YOU WON'T SEE A THING!

FOR THE SAKE OF THE LORD MUST I BEG FOR EVERYTHING?
IF YOU TREATED A DOG LIKE YOU TREAT ME YOU'D BE LOCKED UP
OH I'M SORRY, MY LITTLE SOLDIER! NOW LOOK. I'VE GOT YOU ALL UPSET!

SO...
BLINKING FLIP, MOTHER, I CAN'T SEE A THING. WHY DID YOU MAKE ME WASTE MY MONEY ON IT?
CAH!
WELL, YOU CAN THROW YOUR OWN MONEY AWAY, BUT NOT MINE. THIS IS COMING OUT OF YOUR POCKET, YOU HAGGARD OLD SKINFLINT!

LATER
SNIFF!
WHAT IS IT, MY PRINCE?

YOU BROUGHT ME ON HOLIDAY TO ENJOY MYSELF. YOU'VE GONE OUT OF YOUR WAY TO TURN IT INTO A NIGHTMARE FOR ME. YOU MUST ENTERTAIN ME!
I'M SORRY MY ANGEL. I KNOW. LET'S GO FOR A GAME OF CRAZY GOLF!

CRAZY GOLF? MY GOD, YOU REALLY KNOW HOW TO SPOIL ME, DON'T YOU, MOTHER
COME ON THEN! LET'S GET IT OVER WITH

AT THE CRAZY GOLF...
ONE AND A HALF, PLEASE!
FORTY FIVE PENCE, PLEASE
FORTY FIVE PENCE! FORTY FIVE PENCE! ARE YOU SURE I'M WORTH IT, MOTHER?

BUT...
I MUST BE DREAMING! AM I REALLY EXPECTED TO PLAY WITH THIS, YOU STUPID OLD HAG?
IF I MUST SUFFER THIS ORDEAL, I'M GOING TO DO IT PROPERLY!

20 MINUTES LATER...
GOLF SHOP
COME ON, MOTHER
I JUST HOPE THESE CLUBS ARE GOOD ENOUGH. THERE WERE MORE EXPENSIVE ONES. YOUR PENNY PINCHING WAYS WILL HAVE TO STOP I CAN TELL YOU!

TAP IT THROUGH THE WIND-MILL, TIMMY!
I KNOW

WAP

FLIPPIN' FLIP, YOU'VE RUINED MY SHOT, YOU USELESS OLD TROLL!
I'M SORRY MY LITTLE PIXIE.
IT'S A BIT LATE FOR THAT NOW, ISN'T IT? YOU'RE ALWAYS IN THE WRONG PLACE AT THE WRONG TIME!

40 MINUTES LATER...
HURRY UP, SON, THERE'S A QUEUE FORMING

THAT'S IT! MY CONCENTRATION IS COMPLETELY BROKEN. I DON'T WANT TO PLAY ANYMORE.
DID THE NASTY MAN UPSET YOU, TIMMY?
YES!

LATER...
MOTHER. BUY ME A KITE, BIGGER THAN THAT BOYS OVER THERE
NOW!

I HAVEN'T GOT ANY MONEY LEFT, MY LITTLE BONBON! IT'S ALL SPENT. MUMMY WILL NIP TO THE BANK TOMORROW. YOU CAN HAVE ONE THEN.
OH CAN I?
I MIGHT NOT WANT ONE TOMORROW. I MAY BE DEAD. NOT THAT YOU'D CARE. I SEE YOU HAD ENOUGH MONEY TO BUY YOURSELF A BOOK! SELF, SELF, SELF!

BAH! SHE JUST CAN'T GO ON TREATING ME LIKE THIS. THE SELFISH OLD CRONE!
HRUMPH!

SEVERAL HOURS LATER...
HA!
I'LL PROBABLY DRIFT FOR DAYS BEFORE I'M RESCUED! THAT'LL TEACH THE OLD WITCH!

Norbert Colon
"He's still as Tight as a Gnat's Chuff."

NORBERT IS GOING ON HOLIDAY...

DAMN! I'VE GOT A PUNCTURE!
POP!

JESUS! I'M NOT FALLING FOR THAT ONE AGAIN! I HAD QUITE ENOUGH OF YOU AT FILEY LAST YEAR WHEN YOU HID IN MY SUITCASE!
NOW GET OUT AND FUCK OFF!!

BAH! I WAS REALLY LOOKING FORWARD TO THAT WEEK IN FRANCE TOO. WE WERE GOING ON THE HOVERCRAFT.

MIND YOU- THERE'S NO DOUBT ABOUT IT, HOLIDAYS IS AN EXPENSIVE BUSINESS WHICHEVER WAY YOU LOOK AT IT...
HMM... BUT YOU DO ONLY LIVE ONCE, AFTER ALL...
Come to Barbados.
It's really nice.
...AND YOU CAN'T TAKE IT WITH YOU...

SO...
HEY- THIS IS THE LIFE READERS! A WARM TROPICAL CLIMATE, PLENTY OF EXOTIC FRUIT, A CHANGE OF SCENERY!
I'VE ONLY BEEN HERE THREE DAYS- AND ALREADY I FEEL FABULOUS!

OI! WHAT ARE YOU DOING IN MY GREENHOUSE? AND WHO'S BEEN EATING ALL MY PRIZE TOMATOES?
ERM...

TAKE THIS...
THWACK!
YOWCH!!

ANOTHER PLAN FOILED! WELL I SUPPOSE THERE'S NOTHING FOR IT...
Travel Agents

HAVE YOU GOT ANY LAST-MINUTE STANDBY PACKAGES THAT YOU DON'T WANT- FOR NOTHING?
ERM... NO, NOT REALLY.

BUT ONE OF OUR CHEAPER SUNNY-HOLS PACKAGES AT THE MOMENT IS A WEEK IN BENIDORM HALF-BOARD. PRICES START AT AROUND SIXTY POUNDS.
ACTUALLY- I WAS LOOKING FOR SOMETHING A LITTLE MORE TOWARDS THE CHEAPER END OF THE HOLIDAY MARKET.

HOURS LATER...
HOW ABOUT THIS? A THREE MONTH WORKING CRUISE...
crap-a-tour

GUTTING KELP ON A BELGIAN FACTORY TRAWLER IN THE SOUTH ATLANTIC. YOU'D HAVE TO SLEEP ON THE DECK- BUT THERE'S ALL THE PLANKTON YOU CAN EAT.

IT'S TWO POUNDS FIFTY.
DOES THAT INCLUDE SPENDING MONEY?
NO.
WELL YOU CAN FORGET IT THEN.

I'M NOT GOING TO LINE THEIR POCKETS.
I'M OFF CAMPING.

LOOK AT THAT. ALL THAT BRASS FOR A BIT OF CLOTH.
TENT SHOP
SALE NOW ON
Bargain clearance offer
TENT £1·50
THEY MUST THINK I DROPPED OFF A CHRISTMAS TREE.

CARDBOARD BOXES ARE JUST AS GOOD AS TENTS. AND THEY'RE FREE!

NEXT MORNING...
AHA! HERE'S SOME MORE HOUSEHOLD REFUSE TO BE DISPOSED OF. IT'S A BOX OF SMELLY OLD CLOTHES.
FUDC
!

I'LL START THE CRUSHER.

A FORTNIGHT LATER...
I'M ON A FANTASTIC BIRD-WATCHING HOLIDAY NOW, READERS. THERE'S PLENTY OF THINGS TO SEE, LOTS OF WILDLIFE, AND THE FOOD'S THROWN IN!

MUNICIPAL DUMP

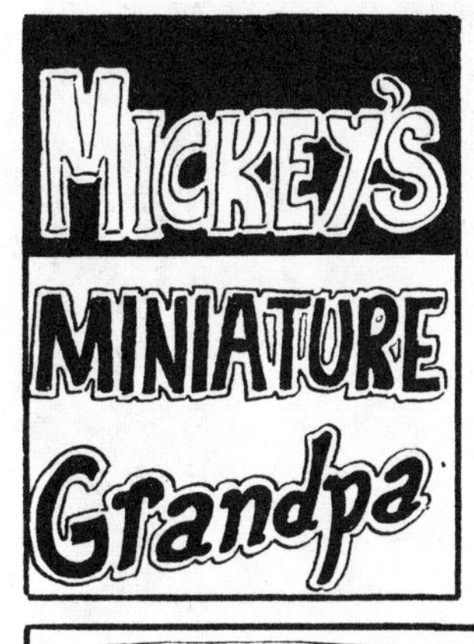


AFTER HAVING AN ARGUMENT WITH A MYSTERIOUS GYPSY, MICKEY MARSTON'S GRANDPA BECAME CONVINCED THAT HE WAS THE VICTIM OF A CURSE WHICH HAD CAUSED HIM TO SHRINK TO A REMARKABLE FOUR INCHES IN HEIGHT!

# I made love to Esther Rantzen in a previous life

**EXCLUSIVE**

Esther (right) as she is today, and (below) as she may have appeared in Egyptian times.

**A bus driver from Berkshire claims to have bedded many of the world's most beautiful women – stars like glamourous TV presenter Esther Rantzen – during previous lives. And now Ron Thompson, 46, has *revealed all* about his sexy exploits in a startling new book. In it he explains how during previous incarnations on Earth, he has met and made love to an incredible bevvy of well-known beauties. Top models, movie actresses, TV personalities and beauty queens! During his many previous lives on Earth, Ron has had them all. And here, in an exclusive excerpt from his book, he spills the beans about his steamy nights of passion with some of the world's sexiest women.**

"I have always been a firm believer in reincarnation, and being a keen spiritualist with considerable psychic powers, I am able to recall vividly my previous incarnations on Earth, going back many hundreds of years.

In one previous manifestation of my spirit I clearly recall being an Egyptian merchant, travelling through the desert many centuries age.

### SNAKE

One day I came across an oasis, so I stopped to water my camel. Nearby there was a tent, so I went in to see if anybody wanted to buy a carpet. Inside a wealthy man was surrounded by a dozen women who where bathing him in oils and feeding him grapes. One of the women began to do erotic dancing with a snake which slithered around the contours of her body. Although I didn't realise it then, I now know that this was in fact TV presenter Esther Rantzen who, during one of her previous lives, had obviously been an Egyptian dancing girl.

### NAVAL

In the yellow glow of the campfire her perfectly formed body was clearly visable through her thin, silk sari. A precious jewel sparkled in her naval. I wanted her more than anything in the world.

The man in the tent agreed to swap her for one of my carpets. Then she took my hand and led me to a nearby tent where we were alone. Hypnotised by her eyes I lay motionless as she undressed me and slowly began to explore my body.

### NAKED

Eventually our naked bodies came together, and there beneath the stars she gave herself to me. We must have made love a hundred times that night, until eventually we fell asleep. The next morning when I awoke she had gone.

### MINE

I suppose it's fairly ironic that mine and Esther Rantzen's paths should have crossed in this way during previous existances. Perhaps I've just been lucky, but there are many other top stars who I have met in this way, among then TV and radio personality Gloria Hunniford.

### DESIRES

I met Gloria during the 19th century at which time I was the gardener on a large country estate. I believe that in her previous incarnation she was married to a local squire. Unfortunately he'd been injured in the army and was unable to satisy her sexual desires.

### HOT

One hot summer's day I was hard at work in the woods when suddenly she appeared, and sat down nearby. After a while she spoke, and although I didn't realise it then, her distinctive Northern Irish accent was

later to become a familiar sound to me as I listened to her popular daytime show on Radio Two.

"You look hot", she said. Sweat dripped from my half naked body. I had been chopping down trees with a large axe, but her eyes gazed down towards another of my tools. "Let's take a dip together in the lake", she said.

As we swam together I could hear the waves gently rippling around her nakedness. Afterwards we lay on the grass to dry. The sun was warm as it shone down upon her beautiful white love mountains. She turned and whispered softly in my ear, "Be gentle with me".

### BODIES

We made love for what seemed like an eternity. Night followed day. I lost all track of time. It was dark and then it was light as our bodies melted into one. I had never experienced anything like it. We kept going for several days until it was finally over, then we both collapsed in a state of complete exhaustion. Gloria came back to my cabin in the woods many times, after that, and I will never forget the passionate days and nights we spent together.

Not many men can claim to have made love to Angela Rippon. Indeed, strictly speaking it would be wrong to say that I had. For that feat was achieved not by me but by another of my former selves – none other than Lord Nelson himself.

### BATTLES

This was perhaps the best known of my previous incarnations, for it was during my life as Nelson that I won numerous sea battles and became a national hero. And it was during this period that I first met Angela Rippon, or Lady Emma Hamilton as she was known in those days.

### TORRID

Our affair was a torrid one. I longed for her while at sea, spending many sleepless nights alone in my hammock. But the time we spent together I will never forget. As Nelson I had suffered many injuries in battle, but I can assure you that my column remained intact.

### PASSION

We made love with all the passion of a raging sea, and then we'd lie together like ships becalmed, gazing into each other's eyes. We were hopelessly in love, and one of my main regrets is that I was killed at the battle of Trafalgar, thus ending our beautiful relationship."

In the next issue:- ***MY OUT-OF-BODY EXPERIENCES*** – Ron reveals how, through meditation, he is now able to "free his spirit" from his body, and experience sexual relationships with many of today's top stars.

COLDBOTZ IS A BOTTOM CORRECTION CENTRE TO WHICH ONLY THE MOST SERIOUS OF BOTTOM OFFENDERS ARE SENT. MANY PEOPLE PASS THROUGH THE FOREBODING GATES, BUT THE ONLY WAY OUT IS IN A WOODEN BOX, FOR NOBODY, YES NOBODY, GETS OUT OF COLDBOTZ ALIVE.

THIS PARTICULAR DAY FINDS THREE MEN TALKING IN THE EXERCISE YARD. SPEAKING OF FORBIDDEN THOUGHTS... THOUGHTS OF LIFE WITHOUT STEEL UNDERPANT TORTURE, A LIFE FREE FROM THE JACK-BOOTED FOOT OF BOTTOM OPRESSION ... THEIR THOUGHTS ARE OF *ESCAPE!*

# MAD AS A HATTER!

**The Queen is losing her marbles. That is the unofficial word from Buckingham Palace as Her Royal Highness begins her 37th year on the throne.**

## The Queen is a fruitcake claims former Palace man

This incredible claim is being made by Roger Thompson, a former Palace employee who says he is desperately worried about Her Majesty's health. Sacked from his job at the Palace for stealing cutlery — a crime which he strenuously denies — Thompson has decided to speak out and make his concerns public, for the Queen's own sake.

"I never stole that cutlery", Roger told us. "It was all a big cover-up, and I took the blame to protect the Queen. Everyone inside the Palace knew that she'd been stealing it herself. She used to hoard it in pillow-cases in her bedroom".

### HUMMING

According to Roger, the Queen had been acting strangely for many months. "On a couple of occasions I'd seen her wandering around the Palace humming strange tunes to herself. Then on another occasion I saw her chasing butterflies around the Palace garden. Nothing unusual about that I thought, until she caught one — and ate it! I mentioned it to Prince Phillip later that day but he told me I had been imagining things".

### SUSPICIONS

A few days later Roger's suspicions were confirmed when the Queen came down to breakfast — dressed as Napoleon. "She ate her breakfast in silence. No-one said a word. Afterwards the staff were told to forget the incident, or it would cost us our jobs".

As Roger recalls, that was one of the last meals the Qeen ate at the Palace. "You see, she was convinced that the chef was trying to poison her and steal the Crown Jewels. I know it sounds crazy, but it's true. At meal-times she would refuse to eat a thing. Eventually she started going out in her royal carriage to buy Chinese take-aways, then she'd take them to the Tower of London and eat them with her eyes firmly fixed on the Crown Jewels".

### CUCUMBER

The Queen's unusual behaviour was beginning to cause some embarrassment in public. "I remember one royal garden party in particular", Roger told us. "She refused to touch the cucumber sandwiches in case they were poisoned, and she was mingling with the guests eating Kentucky Fried Chicken out of a huge red and white party bucket, then wiping her fingers on her dress. The guests were clearly embarrassed".

## She dresses as Napoleon – and barks like a dog

Over the weeks Roger noticed the Queen's condition was deteriorating. "The next thing that happened really set me worrying. I was awoken one night by the sound of a dog howling and barking. It was a terrible sound, and what made it all the more eerie was the full moon outside.

### LETTUCE

I got up and as I walked along the corridor the Queen rushed past me on all fours, barking ferociously. I followed her down to the kitchen where I found her underneath a table — feeding small bits of cheese to mice".

### DUNGEONS

On another occasion the Queen summoned Mrs Thatcher to the Palace and told her to invade France. The Prime Minister explained that we were members of the EEC, and that we couldn't go to war with France. Furious, she told the Guards to take Mrs Thatcher down to the dungeons and have her stretched! They took her away and locked her in a cell, then, after a couple of days when the Queen had forgotten about it, they let her go".

Trying to start a war was just one of the Queen's many unusual requests. As Roger recalls, another was calling for a Court Jester! "She was bored with watching the telly one night, so she demanded a Jester be summoned to entertain her. We rang a theatrical agency and they sent round a top TV comic and talent show host to do his act. Of course the Queen insisted he dress authentically — in a funny hat with pointy shoes with bells on the end.

### TOWER

The poor bloke must have felt a proper fool, but he did his act anyway. At the end there was complete silence. The Queen was not amused. She told the Guards to take him to the Tower of London and behead him the next day! Luckily, by the morning she'd forgotten about it, so they let the poor fellow go. But that was one night he will never forget. Although he probably has done by now".

According to Roger steps are now taken to avoid situations like that. "For most of her public appearances, they use a double — that woman who looks like the Queen usually stands in for her. The Queen herself spends most of her time in her bedroom, watching game shows on TV. She wears sunglasses and keeps the room in total darkness. If you saw her today you wouldn't recognise her.

### FINGERNAILS

She must weigh all of 18 stone, and she eats Kentucky Fried Chicken virtually non-stop. Her fingernails are 2 feet long, and her hair almost reaches the floor. She only ever leaves the room to visit the bathroom, and every time she insists that a new carpet is laid in the corridor so she doesn't catch any germs. As another precaution she wears a surgical mask and a pair of brightly coloured fisherman's waders. Getting in and out of this ridiculous costume takes her so long that a single visit to the bathroom can take up to 4 hours".

### ● FOOTNOTE

Roger Thompson pleaded guilty to the charge of stealing cutlery at Bow Street Magistrates Court yesterday, and asked for 173 similar offences to be taken into account. He was remanded in custody for 14 days pending psychiatric reports.

Finbarr Saunders
FNARR! FNARR!
& his
DOUBLE ENTENDRES!

IT'S HOLIDAY TIME ONCE MORE...
HURRY UP THERE FINBARR! TSK! TSK! YOU AND YOUR LUGGAGE! HAVEN'T YOU PUT IT IN YET?
ARF! ARF!
TENT
K-YAK! K-YAK!

I REALLY CAN'T IMAGINE WHY YOU'VE BROUGHT THAT KITE ALONG.
YOU'LL PROBABLY NOT HAVE A CHANCE TO TAKE IT OUT- NEVER MIND GET IT UP!

IT'LL NEED QUITE A BREEZE AND YOU'LL BE LUCKY IF YOU GET A STIFF ONE AT THIS TIME OF YEAR.
FWOOO! FWOOO!
HO! HO!
YIKK! YIKK!

WASN'T IT NICE OF MR. GIMLET TO LEND US HIS TENT WHILST HE WENT OFF IN HIS CARAVAN!
A69
TENT
HARR! HARR!
WOO! WOO!

AT THE CAMPING SITE...
THIS LOOKS LIKE A GOOD SPOT TO ERECT IT. DO YOU SUPPOSE IT'LL FIT?
AYE BUT YOU'LL END UP SLEEPING ON A THISTLE.
SNUT! SNUT!
HO! HO!
AG! AG!
TENT
OOH. AFTER LAYING ON ONE FOR A FEW NIGHTS, YOU HARDLY NOTICE IT. AND I'VE HAD MORE PRICKS THAN YOU'VE HAD HOT DINNERS!
FNARR! FNARR!

LATER...
5...4...3 ...2...1...
?
YOOHOO!

GOODNESS GRACIOUS! WHAT A REMARKABLE COINCIDENCE. FANCY MR. GIMLET COMING TO EXACTLY THE SAME SITE AS US! I THOUGHT HE WAS GOING TO LOOK UP AN OLD FRIEND AND TAKE THEM OUT TO FEELHAM-ON-THE-HILL IN CHESHIRE!
!
NUFF! NUFF!
KWAH! KWAH!
WOOOO! WOOOO!

HAVE YOU HAD A GOOD JOURNEY WITH YOUR CARAVAN?
YES, MIND YOU- IT'S LARGER THAN I'M USED TO, AND IT TAKES QUITE A BIT OF PULLING!
ARP! ARP! ARF! ARP!
PERHAPS YOU'D LIKE A CUP OF COFFEE- DO YOU FANCY ONE?

OH NO! I FORGOT TO PACK A STOVE!
NEVER MIND, I'VE GOT A SPARE ONE IN THE CARAVAN. I'LL BRING IT OVER TO YOUR TENT. JUST OPEN YOUR FLAPS A LITTLE SO AS I CAN POP IT IN!!
PHOOOARRR!!

LET'S MAKE A REAL CAMP FIRE, EH FINBARR? WE CAN COOK SOME FRESH SHELLFISH ONCE WE'VE CUT SOME WOOD. HERE- HOLD THE SHAFT OF MY CHOPPER FIRMLY.
GWOOA! GWOOA!
HAF! HAF!
GOOR! GOOOR!

SHORTLY...
NOW THEN, TAKE HOLD OF THE TWO STICKS. NOW WE'LL RUB THE ENDS TOGETHER. DO IT BRISKLY - OR NOTHING WILL HAPPEN.
WOOOF! WOOOF!
SNORT! SNORT!
PHWOOOAARR!
FNARR! FNARR!

WHAT A LOVELY BLAZE! WHEN I'M BY THE SEASIDE, I LOVE THE TASTE OF A HOT WINKLE!
YAK! YAK!
KWOOOPH! KWOOOPH!

MILK OR CREAM MR. GIMLET? IF YOU WANT SOME, I'LL NIP BACK INTO THE TENT AND GET MY JUGS OUT.
THAT'S OKAY.
BWROOOOOAAARR!!

ME AND FINBARR ARE GOING DOWN TO THE BEACH.
MY WIFE AND I HAVE BOX KITES - AND I OFTEN TAKE HERS OUT WHEN I'M AT A LOOSE END.
ARF! ARF!
HO! HO!

SO...
REMEMBER - IF IT STARTS TO DROOP, PULL ON IT A BIT, AND IT'LL BE STRAIGHT UP AGAIN!
FNURK! FNURK!
KWA! KWA!
YUP! YUP!
AG! AG! AG! AG!

KEEP A FIRM GRIP ON YOUR END. IF YOU LET YOUR ATTENTION WANDER, IT'LL GO SLACK.

FNARRR! FNARRR!
YUKK! YUKK!
HAK! HAK!
HOOF! HOOF!

YOU SEE - NOW YOU'VE ALLOWED IT TO DROP IN THE SEA. YOU'D BE WISE TO DRY THE DOWEL. IT GOES ALL SALTY AND THE END SPLITS. MIND YOU- I'VE PLAYED WITH MY WIFE'S BOX - AND I'VE DIPPED IT A FEW TIMES, I CAN TELL YOU.
!

THAT REMINDS ME - I'M OFF TO SEE YOUR MOTHER. PERHAPS YOU'D LIKE TO QUEUE FOR SOME ICES. I DON'T KNOW WHAT YOUR MOTHER WANTS BUT MINE'S A LARGE ONE WITH CRUSHED NUTS!
YAAARGH! YAAARGH!
HOFF! HOFF!

1 HOUR LATER...
ARE YOU GOING TO GET ON TOP NOW MR. GIMLET?
NO - KEEP BLOWING. IT'S STILL GETTING BIGGER.
HO! HO! IT SOUNDS LIKE MR. GIMLET AND MUM ARE INFLATING THE LILO!

## Passion and Heartache in the

# Tent of Love

***It looked like being a long, lonely summer for young Tricia Jones when she split up with boyfriend Adam Hartley. But plucky Tricia had other plans . . .***

After a long cycle journey they arrived at the field in the countryside.
HERE WE ARE, THIS IS THE FIELD. NICE ISN'T IT.
YEAH, FINE.
I'LL PITCH MY TENT OVER THERE.

OH, ADAM. YOU WON'T BELIEVE THIS, BUT I'VE FORGOTTEN MY TENT.

I'LL JUST HAVE TO SHARE YOURS.
OH, I SUPPOSE SO. BUT THERE'S NOTHING BETWEEN US, REMEMBER. NO STRINGS.

Soon they had settled in.
SAY, ADAM. I'M STARVING. HOW ABOUT I COOK US A NICE MEAL FOR TWO, EH?

LOOK, I'VE BROUGHT SOME CANDLES AND A'BOTTLE OF WINE.
NO THANKS, TRICIA.

I'M GOING TO GET A TIN OF BEANS ON THE GO. BUT YOU CAN USE THE STOVE AFTER ME IF YOU LIKE.
NO THANKS. I'VE JUST LOST MY APPETITE.

Later
ADAM, LET'S GO DOWN TO THE VILLAGE PUB FOR A NICE QUIET DRINK TOGETHER. THEY'VE GOT REAL LOG FIRES AND . . .
NO TA! I'M TURNING IN EARLY TRY NOT TO WAKE ME UP WHEN YOU GET BACK, EH?

OH ADAM, THAT REMINDS ME, I'VE FORGOTTEN MY SLEEPING BAG IS THERE ANY CHANCE I COULD . . .

FORGET IT.
I BROUGHT A SPARE.
HUMPH!

Slightly disappointed, Tricia wandered off to the pub alone.
NO LUCK SO FAR. I'LL HAVE TO PUT PLAN B INTO ACTION — AND TRY TO MAKE HIM JEALOUS.

At closing time . . .
LISTEN . . . ERM . . . BENNY. FANCY COMING BACK TO MY TENT FOR COFFEE.
OOO-ARRR!

I'M SHARING MY TENT WITH A FRIEND. BUT DON'T WORRY ABOUT HIM. HE'LL PROBABLY BE ASLEEP.
OOO-ARRR!

Back at the tent . . .
YOU DON'T MIND IF BENNY STAYS THE NIGHT DO YOU?
EH?
YOU DID SAY WE WERE FREE AGENTS, REMEMBER?

COME ON BENNY, MAKE YOURSELF AT HOME.
THIS IS OUR SLEEPING BAG HERE.

OOOO-OOOOO-OOOOO-ARRRR!
OH . . . YES . . . YES . . . UH . . . UH . . .
I DON'T BELIVE IT! ADAM'S GONE TO SLEEP. HE HASN'T EVEN NOTICED US.
ZZZZZZZZZZ!

The next morning . . .
OOOOAGH!
THAT'S ODD . . . WHERE'S ADAM?
AAAGH!

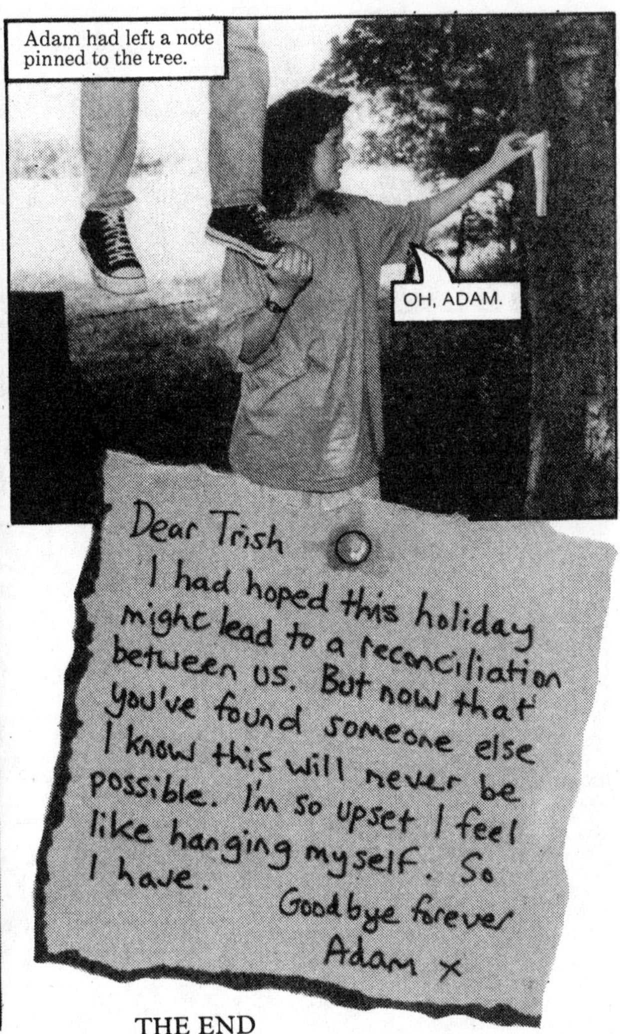


THE END

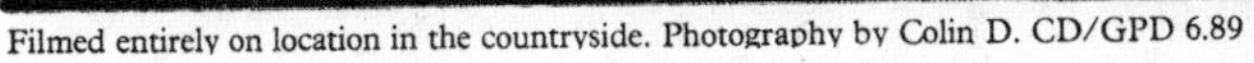

Filmed entirely on location in the countryside. Photography by Colin D. CD/GPD 6.89

If all your shit had to be taken away in milk bottles
it would need an entire milk float just to remove
the excrement produced in one month alone
by an average family of four. Probably.

**The Ten Water Businesses of England and Wales**

*Taking your shit away – and putting it in the sea*

Issued by Kleinman, Bollocks and Shitehouse on behalf of H.M. Government, who are flogging the water board to make a few bob.

"I have absolutely no recollection of anything that happened after 9 p.m. last night. **Thanks very much!**" B.K. Glasgow

"This morning I awoke with my head in the fridge, the kettle had melted on the stove and I have vomit in the turn-ups of my trousers. **What a smashing beer!**" A.M. Newcastle

"I came around at about 8.30 a.m. in a police cell, I had dried blood on my shirt and my trousers were cold and damp with urine. I have been charged with Drunk and Disorderly. **Cheers!** I would recommend your fine beer to anyone!" F.W. Birmingham

"I have appalling diarrhoea and my bottom lip has turned green. I am in hospital being treated for serious head injuries. Is your **magnificent ale** available in cans?" D.P. Manchester

"... I had locked my three children in the coal house and later awoke in my neighbour's dog's kennel with a galvanised steel bucket on my head. I have no money left. My wife has left me. **Your beer is a winner!**" J.F. Stockport

"I cannot remember my own name. Where am I? God help me I think I'm dying. **What a beer! What a beer! Thanks!**" Anon. Sunderland

**A Harmfully Strong Traditional Ale**

**DR. O'REILLY'S Blitzkreig ME 109**

Dr. O'Reilly's Beers and Agrochemicals Ltd, Unit 6, Purston Industrial Estate, West Yorks.

# BUSTER GONAD AND HIS *Unfeasibly* LARGE TESTICLES

GPD. CD. JT. SD. 89.

MAXWELL STRAKER- RECORD BREAKER!
YOU'VE GOT TO HAVE DEDICATION -OO OH OH- DEDICATION...

MAX!! GET UP!! IT'S NEARLY TIME FOR SCHOOL!

BAH! MRS. THERESA CHURCH OF MICHIGAN USA STAYED IN BED FOR 25 YEARS, AND NOW MY ATTEMPT HAS BEEN SCUPPERED AFTER ONLY EIGHT HOURS!!

HRUMPH! STILL A GOOD FIVE FEET TO GO YET!
ROBERT WADLOW OF ALTON ILLINOIS WAS 6 FOOT 5 AT THE AGE OF 10, AND 8 FOOT 11 WHEN HE DIED!

SHORTLY...
WHAT DO YOU WANT FOR BREAKFAST?
14 HARD-BOILED EGGS.
I'LL EAT THEM IN LESS THAN 14.42 SECONDS- THEREBY BEATING JOHN KENMUIR'S 1987 RECORD!

DON'T BE SO GREEDY- HERE HAVE SOME BEANS.

COCKTAIL STICK INDEED! WHY CAN'T YOU USE A KNIFE AND FORK LIKE ANY NORMAL CHILD?
munch munch

PRESENTLY...
STRAIGHT TO SCHOOL NOW MAX. NO PUSHING A PEA ALONG THE ROAD WITH YOUR NOSE AGAIN.
AW.

HOWEVER...
HEY - THAT GIVES ME AN IDEA. I COULD BE THE MOST TATTOOED MAN IN THE WORLD!
TATTOOS

HELLO - CAN YOU TATTOO OVER NINETY-SEVEN PER CENT OF MY BODY SURFACE PLEASE?

5 MINUTES LATER...
I'M SORRY - BUT THAT'S ALL YOU GET FOR 75p.
?
BUT IT'S ALL THE DINNER MONEY I'VE GOT. BAH! I'M NEVER GOING TO GET IN THE BOOK AT THIS RATE.

LATER...
HOW ON EARTH ARE WE GOING TO GET RID OF ALL THESE OLD BARRELS?
BREWERY
USED BARREL DISPOSAL DEPT.
AHA! THEY GIVE ME A CHAMPION 24-CARAT RECORD-BUSTING NOTION!

PRESENTLY, AT THE ICE RINK...
A HALF PLEASE - AND CAN I HIRE SOME SKATES?
AYE - THROUGH THERE SONNY.

WHERE D'YOU THINK YOU'RE GOING WITH THAT?
I'M GOING TO JUMP 19 OF THEM. THE REST ARE IN THE CAR PARK - CAN YOU GIVE ME A HAND?
To the Ice

AH WELL - NEVER MIND. THERE'S STILL PLENTY OF OTHER RECORDS JUST ASKING TO BE BROKEN!
I'M OFF TO FARMER GILES'S COW FIELD.

STEVE URNER OF CALIFORNIA ONCE THREW A FRESH COWPAT 266 FEET. I'M SURE I CAN BETTER THAT!!

OOH! IT'S THERE!!
LOB
IT'S THERE!!

!
THAP!

OORS! IT'S FARMER GILES- AND HE'S GOT A PITCHFORK.
GRRRRR.
ming!

NER! NER! NER! NER!
AMBULANCE

NEXT DAY...
MAX BECK ONCE COVERED HIMSELF WITH A MANTLE OF 100,000 BEES!
Golden Syrup
THERE MUST EASY BE A MILLION BEES IN THAT NEST!

HO! HO! MY CATAPULT SHOULD ROUSE THEM!
THUD!
GOLDEN SYRUP
WAP
GUINESS HALL OF FAME - HERE I COME!

OH NO!! THEY LOOK LIKE AFRICAN RED HORNET WASPS- AND I'VE PROVOKED THEM INTO A KILLING FRENZY!!

NER! NER! NER! NER!

TWO DAYS LATER, IN HOSPITAL...
WELL DONE MAX! MR. BORIS McSQUIRTER HERE HAS FINALLY PUT YOU IN THE RECORD BOOK!
GREAT! HAVE I SURVIVED THE GREATEST NUMBER OF HORNET WASP STINGS?
NO - I'M AFRAID YOU MISSED THAT RECORD - BY ONE STING.

CONGRATULATIONS YOUNG MAN! YOU NOW HOLD THE RECORD FOR BEING BRITAIN'S DAFTEST CUNT!
HEY WOW!

FULCHESTER UTD, UNDER THREAT OF INSOLVENCY, HAVE RAISED ENOUGH MONEY TO SAVE THE CLUB WITH A SHAKIN' STEVENS BENEFIT CONCERT. BUT - NO SOONER HAVE THE TAKINGS BEEN COUNTED - A MILLION POUNDS - THAN THE MONEY VANISHES...

BUT NO! SHAKEY'S SKILFUL FLICK HAS WRONG-FOOTED THE GRIMBLEDON DEFENCE!
YES. AND HE'S PUT FLEETFOOT WINGER BROWN FOX IN THE CLEAR!

SHE BEATS ONE MAN...
AND ANOTHER!

SHE'S NUTMEGGED THE GRIMBLEDON No. 3 TO REACH THE DEAD BALL LINE.
3

CAN SHE GET THE BALL IN?
YES!

IT LOOKS LIKE A TELLING CROSS!
YES. IT COULD PAY DIVIDENDS IF SOMEONE CAN GET ON THE END OF IT AND DO THE DAMAGE WHERE IT MATTERS - IN THE SIX YARD BOX.

NO... IT'S TOO DEEP.
IT'S GONE WAY OVER THE HEADS OF THE FULCHESTER FORWARDS.

BUT...
WOW!!
BLAM
THE LAD HUCKNALL OUT OF SIMPLY RED HAS COME FROM NOWHERE - AND UNLEASHED A FEROCIOUS VOLLEY!!
GOAL!!

FANTASTIC SHOT!
HOORAY FOR MICK OUT OF SIMPLY RED!

AFTER THE RESTART, FULCHESTER QUICKLY HAMMER HOME THE ADVANTAGE WITH ANOTHER GOAL.
A PILEDRIVER FROM THE TRANSPARENT LEFT FOOT OF JOHNNY X!
IT'S THERE!!

AND ANOTHER...
THE FULCHESTER FORWARDS ARE TEARING THE GRIMBLEDON DEFENCE APART LIKE BUTTER!
THREE NIL!

AND ANOTHER...
PROFESSOR WÖLFGANG SCHNELL BSc. PhD'S TRIGONOMETRICALLY CALCULATED HEADER PLACES UNITED FIRMLY IN THE DRIVING SEAT.
GREAT GOAL!!

THAT'S FOUR NIL SYD. WE'RE MAKING INROADS ON THE FLANKS AND DOMINATING THE FIELD IN THE KEY AREAS.
ABSOLUTELY BOSS. AND NOW IF WE CAN ONLY MAINTAIN THIS FOUR GOAL MARGIN OVER GRIMBLEDON, IT'LL SEE US SAFELY BACK IN THE FIRST DIVISION, ON AGGREGATE.

UNITED PUSH FORWARD AGAIN FOR A FIFTH GOAL - TO PUT THE RESULT BEYOND DOUBT...
IT'S A GOLDEN OPPORTUNITY!
AN OPEN GOAL!
HUCKNALL OUT OF SIMPLY RED MUST SCORE!!

THE KEEPER COMMITTED HIMSELF TOO EARLY!
HE'S LEFT THE GOALMOUTH COMPLETELY UNGUARDED - THERE'S NO WAY THE FLAME-HAIRED MINSTREL OF SOUL IS GOING TO MISS THIS ONE!

OOOH! HE'S SKIED IT OVER THE BAR!
YES.

SECONDS LATER - THE TOUSLE-LOCKED SONGSTER GETS A CHANCE TO REDEEM HIMSELF
A PINPOINT DEFENCE-SPLITTING PASS FROM THE BUXOM SQUAW.
HUCKNALL OUT OF SIMPLY RED ONLY HAS THE KEEPER TO BEAT!

BUT
BOO!
HISS!
WHAT A LOAD OF RUBBISH!
HOOF!
IN A SADLY IRONIC ECHO OF HIS MUSICAL CAREER MICK HUCKNALL OUT OF SIMPLY RED'S PROMISING EARLY SUCCESS HAS BEEN FOLLOWED UP WITH A SERIES OF LACKLUSTRE DISAPPOINTMENTS.

THE FULL-TIME WHISTLE!
PEEP!
FULCHESTER WIN BY A CLEAR FOUR GOALS!

BACK IN DIVISION ONE, IT LOOKS LIKE OUR PROBLEMS ARE OVER EH SYD?
NO BOSS.
I THINK YOU OUGHT TO SEE THIS!

GASP!
I SLEPT WITH TOMMY BROWN
SOCCER SHOCKER
BY PAMELA SLAG

Will THIS SPELL THE END FOR FULCHESTER?
Could THESE SORDID REVELATIONS IN THE PRESS FORCE TOMMY BROWN'S RESIGNATION?
*
DON'T MISS THE NEXT EPISODE!!

FIRST IMPRESSIONS
Young Alan Barber and Judy Sims had been going steady for several months. Everything had been wonderful until one day . . .
ALAN. HOW WOULD YOU FEEL ABOUT COMING TO MEET MY PARENTS ON SUNDAY?
OH, NOT YET, JUDY. IT'S A BIT EARLY FOR THAT. IN ANY CASE, I'VE GOT OTHER PLANS.

OH PLEASE ALAN IT WOULD MEAN SO MUCH TO ME.
AND BESIDES, I'VE ALREADY TOLD THEM YOU'RE COMING.

IS THERE NO WAY I CAN GET OUT OF IT?
I'M AFRAID NOT, ALAN. IT MEANS A LOT TO ME. I'LL CALL FOR YOU AT TWELVE.

Alan spent the rest of the day worrying about his date with Judith's folks.
THIS IS A BAD IDEA. THEY'RE BOUND TO HATE ME.
THEY'LL TRY AND TURN HER AGAINST ME BECAUSE OF THE WAY I LOOK.

WELL THEY WON'T SUCCEED.
BY THE TIME I MEET HER PARENTS ON SUNDAY, THEY WON'T HAVE ANY REASON TO DISLIKE ME!

The next day . . .
Gents Hairdresser
WELL, HERE GOES. IT'S A BIG SACRIFICE, BUT IT'S WORTH IT FOR JUDY.

Shortly . . .
WELL, NOW I'VE STARTED I MAY AS WELL GO THE WHOLE HOG AND GET MYSELF A SUIT.

So . . .
THIS ONE IS FIVE HUNDRED POUNDS, SIR.
FIVE HUND . . .?
OH WHAT THE HELL, I'LL TAKE IT!

THERE GOES MY ENTIRE LIFE SAVINGS, BUT IT'LL BE WORTH IT. I'M DETERMINED TO MAKE THE RIGHT IMPRESSION.

Photography by Colin D. CD/GPD 7.89.

THE END

Helpful Herbert
But his good deeds always get him into scrapes!!

HELLO THERE HERBERT. WILL YOU DO ME A FAVOUR?
YES. OF COURSE!

I'VE JUST BOUGHT THESE JACKBOOTS FROM A WARTIME MEMORABILIA SHOP. WILL YOU WALK ABOUT IN THEM FOR AN HOUR, TO BREAK THEM IN?
IF THEY START TO CREAK, RUB THIS PETROLEUM JELLY INTO THE LEATHER.

?
YOO HOO!

HERBERT - MY SON IS AT THE CUB HUT AND HIS PET DOG HAS GIVEN BIRTH. WOULD YOU FETCH HIM HOME - AS HE SO WANTED TO SEE THE LITTER?
YES. OF COURSE!
YIP! YIP!
HE'D REALLY BEST COME HOME ANYWAY, AS HE'S GOT EXAMS AND LATELY HE'S NOT BEEN KEEPING UP WITH HIS REVISION.

HEY! WHAT AN IDEAL OPPORTUNITY. I CAN KILL TWO BIRDS WITH ONE STONE!
EXCUSE ME...

WHAT'S WRONG?
BOO HOO. MY KITE'S STUCK IN A TREE AND IT WON'T COME DOWN!
DON'T WORRY. I'LL GET IT FOR YOU.

HERE, CATCH!
HOORAY FOR HERBERT!

SNAP!
OOER!
READER'S VOICE
CRUMBS. THAT'S A BRAMBLE BUSH!

CRIPES! ALL MY CLOTHES GOT RIPPED OFF!

THANK GOODNESS I FOUND THIS OLD BARREL.
HERBERT...

CAN YOU TAKE THIS OLD SCOOTER ALONG TO THE LOCAL TIP, AS I SIMPLY CAN'T BE BOTHERED.
CERTAINLY.

BUT...

OH LUMME! I'VE GOT SOME GRIT IN MY EYE!!
WINK
BLINK
SCOOT! SCOOT!

WOOO-OOAHH!

FULCHES LAUND COMPA
OOOF!
WHUM!

STRUGGLE
UMF!!
WRESTLE
OOER!
WHOOPS!
EH?
OOO!
AH!

OOH! THAT WAS LUCKY. THE LAUNDRY PROVIDED A SOFT LANDING.

AH! THERE'S THE CUB HUT - BUT I CAN'T SEE ANYONE AROUND. PERHAPS THEY'RE IN THE SHOWER BLOCK!

'ELLO 'ELLO 'ELLO. WHAT'S ALL THIS THEN?

IT'S ALRIGHT OFFICER, I CAN EXPLAIN EVERYTHING. I'M LOOKING FOR A YOUNG BOY SCOUT. HE'S GOT A LITTLE BEHIND AND I WANT TO TAKE HIM HOME TO SEE SOME PUPPIES.
!

IN THAT CASE, I THINK YOU'D BETTER ACCOMPANY ME TO THE STATION.
OH CRUMBS!

# IT'S JUG MANIA!

## Britain's bridegrooms are nutty about knockers – claims vicar

**Fellas are falling over themselves to marry women with big boobs! That's the view of vicar Dennis Randall. And he should know — he's been marrying couples for over forty years.**

Dennis has just completed a book in which he relates many interesting stories derived from his time as a vicar. In it he compares the changing tastes of British bridegrooms over the years, as seen first hand from the altar.

### HITCHED

"When I first started back in the forties, the fellas were going for anything they could get their hands on", Dennis confided. "Like everything else in those days, good looking birds were in short supply. I felt sorry for some of the blokes — they were coming home and getting hitched to the first girl they met off the boat. I'm not kidding, there was some funny looking brides about in those days. Lots of them had been working for the war effort — in factories and in the fields. Some of them were built like cart horses. Today's body builders are nothing compared to these girls".

### COUPLES

Dennis has lost count of the number of couples he has brought together over the years. But he recalls a definate drop in the number of marriages taking place during the late sixties.

Vicar Dennis — he's seen it all

"It was all this love and peace business. Couples weren't bothering to tie the knot. And in those days if a couple did get married, chances are the bride wouldn't even wear a bra. Women's Lib I think they called it. Mind you it had its advantages — I got more than a few eyefulls in those days I can tell you".

In recent years Dennis says the trend is definately towards bigger busts! "Nowadays fellas want something they can get to grips with. I see them every week. The knockers just seem to get bigger and bigger".

Royal Weddings can have an amazing influence on marriages in the months that follow. "Andrew and Fergie was by far the best example", Dennis told us. "The minute those two had walked up the aisle, my church was chock-a-block with fellas all wanting to marry birds with fat arses".

### JUGS

But big hasn't always been considered beautiful. Back in the seventies Dennis detected a definate trend away from buxom brides. "Small jugs were very much the order of the day", he told us.

### VASES

Indeed, Dennis believes a lot of today's broken marriages and divorces can be attributed to bad choice on the part of the bridegroom.

"On a few occasions I felt like asking the bridegroom what on earth he was playing at. Some of the boilers I've hitched up you just wouldn't believe . I know a looker when I see one. Fellas have got to remember — marriage is for life. So if you are getting hitched, make sure you choose a good looking bird".

### TEAPOTS

So far Dennis has failed in his attempts to find a publisher for his book, provisionally entitled 'Here Come the Boobs'. Meanwhile a church spokesman, who denied any knowledge of the book, told us that Rev Randall had been suspended from his job as vicar some time ago pending the outcome of a police enquiry into allegations of Gross Indecency and Sending Pornographic Material through the post.



## Tailors Shop Joke

If you spent hundreds of pounds on a skiing holiday, and then found yourself being harrassed from dawn till dusk by cameramen and reporters, you wouldn't be too pleased, would you? The Royal Family work damn hard for their money. And just like anyone else, when they take a holiday, they deserve some peace and quiet.

*But who pays for their holidays anyway? That's right. We, the taxpayers, do. And as taxpayers we demand to know how our money is being spent. So come on Charles. Grow up.*

**If you don't like cameramen, you shouldn't have been a Prince in the first place.**

We applaud the Government's decision to build the Channel Tunnel. Critics say it's too expensive. That's rubbish. It provides jobs for the unemployed – and is a massive boost for British industry.

*But why France? Why not build it to the Falkland Islands? They are British after all.*

**It's inevitable that if we build a tunnel to France, sooner of later the French are going to want to use it themselves.**

At last the Government have done something about football hooligans. They've introduced a compulsory membership card scheme.

*But membership cards alone won't stop a determined soccer thug. These people are terrorists, not hooligans. And they should be treated as such.*

**We should round them up like cattle, and shoot them like pigs.**

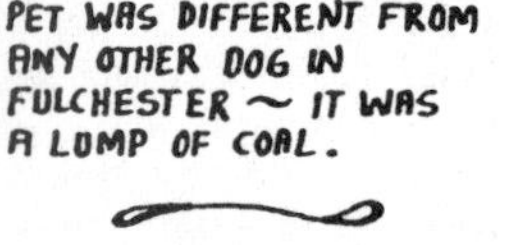


YOUNG ROGER'S REMARKABLE PET WAS DIFFERENT FROM ANY OTHER DOG IN FULCHESTER ~ IT WAS A LUMP OF COAL.

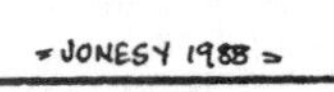

JONESY 1988

OH, DEAR, I DON'T FANCY YOURS MUCH... IT'S THE

# FAT SLAGS

Barney Brimstone's
BISCUIT TIN CIRCUS
Young evacuee Barney Brimstone was the luckiest lad in the remote Scottish fishing village of Invermuir — for he had a biscuit tin with a difference. Unlike his pals' biscuit tins, Barney's contained a fabulous miniature circus.

One fine morning . . .
MMM. WHAT A SMASHING KIPPER!
COUGH! CHOKE! HELLO - WHAT'S THIS?

WHY - IT APPEARS TO BE A ROLL OF TOP SECRET MICROFILM.

After breakfast, Barney went to the harbour to investigate.

Old Robbie McDougall was mending his fishing nets.
HELLO MR. MCDOUGALL. DO YOU KNOW WHICH BOAT BROUGHT THIS KIPPER IN?
MM. NOW LET ME SEE . . .

OCH AYE. I RECKON IT WAS CAUGHT BY THAT WEE TRAWLER OVER YON. THE NORTH STAR.

Barney went over to take a closer look.
THAT'S STRANGE. I'VE NEVER SEEN THIS BOAT IN THE HARBOUR BEFORE.

AND THIS PAINT IS STILL WET.
NORTH STAR
WAIT A MINUTE - WHAT'S THIS? HMM. IT'S THE STRANGEST TRAWLER I'VE EVER SEEN.

THERE'S SOMETHING FUNNY GOING ON - AND I'VE GOT TO GET TO THE BOTTOM OF IT.
IF ONLY I COULD GET ON BOARD WITHOUT THE GUARDS SPOTTING ME.

AND PERHAPS I CAN - WITH THE AID OF MY FABULOUS BISCUIT TIN CIRCUS!

With a crack of his ringmaster's whip, Barney summoned his juggling spider and Coco the caterpillar.
ALLEZ OOP!

Barney kept himself well hidden as his chums headed off towards the boat.

The well trained insects knew exactly what to do.
NORTH STAR

While the guards were distracted by Coco's comical antics, Barney climbed up the rope that his spider had spun, and onto the deck.
ACHTUNG - VOT IST DAS?
HANS, LOOK AT DER FUNNY CATERPILLAR.

HE IS FUNNY, JA?
HO HO.
WAIT A MINUTE. THEY'RE NOT FISHERMEN - THEY'RE NAZI SPIES.
BUT WHAT WOULD SPIES WANT WITH A BARREL OF KIPPERS? HMM. I WONDER . .

Barney tossed one of the fish over the side of the boat.

AHA! JUST AS I THOUGHT! IT'S HEADING STRAIGHT FOR GERMANY!

SO THAT'S THEIR GAME. THE EVIL KRAUTS ARE USING TRAINED HOMING KIPPERS TO SMUGGLE TOP SECRET MICROFILM BACK TO THE FATHERLAND.